CHARLES MERYON

PRINTS & DRAWINGS

CHARLES MERYON

PRINTS

&

DRAWINGS

CATALOGUE BY JAMES D. BURKE

TOLEDO MUSEUM OF ART · TOLEDO · OHIO
29 September · 27 October, 1974

YALE UNIVERSITY ART GALLERY · NEW HAVEN · CONNECTICUT
21 November, 1974 · 19 January, 1975

ST. LOUIS ART MUSEUM · ST. LOUIS · MISSOURI
14 February · 6 April, 1975

Funds from the National Endowment for the Arts, a federal agency,
aided the preparation of the exhibition and the
publication of this catalogue.

Library of Congress Catalogue Card Number: 74-82945

COMPOSED BY MACKENZIE AND HARRIS, INC., SAN FRANCISCO, CALIFORNIA.
PRINTED BY THE MERIDEN GRAVURE COMPANY, MERIDEN, CONNECTICUT.
AT THE CARL PURINGTON ROLLINS OFFICE OF THE YALE UNIVERSITY PRINTING SERVICE.

Designed by Leonard Baskin.

FOREWORD

This is the first comprehensive exhibition devoted to the art of Charles Meryon since The MacGeorge Collection was shown at M. Knoedler and Co. in New York in 1917. Since that time, a few discerning collectors have continued to acquire prints and drawings by this famous French etcher; American museums are now the beneficiaries of this collecting. So extensive are the American collections of this artist's work that they often surpass the holdings of the major European museums in number and quality.

James D. Burke of the Yale Art Gallery has studied Meryon's works in American museums and made the selection for this exhibition. Since Meryon's procedure was thorough and scrupulous, preliminary drawings for many of his prints have survived. Whenever possible, these have been included in the exhibition along with the progressive proofs of Meryon's most famous views of Paris and other subjects. Hence, the serious visitor to this exhibition is provided with an opportunity to study the artist's working method and the ways in which he developed his final, haunting images. Most important, the fascinating work of Meryon is being made available to the American public for the first time in almost 60 years.

OTTO WITTMAN
Director
The Toledo Museum of Art

ALAN SHESTACK
Director
Yale University Art Gallery

CHARLES E. BUCKLEY
Director
The St. Louis Art Museum

LENDERS TO THE EXHIBITION

ANONYMOUS · BOSTON PUBLIC LIBRARY · MUSEUM OF FINE ARTS ·
BOSTON · BOWDOIN COLLEGE MUSEUM OF ART · BRUNSWICK · MAINE ·
THE ART INSTITUTE OF CHICAGO · THE CLEVELAND
MUSEUM OF ART · DETROIT INSTITUTE OF ARTS · FOGG ART
MUSEUM · HARVARD UNIVERSITY · CAMBRIDGE · MASSACHUSETTS ·
METROPOLITAN MUSEUM OF ART · NEW YORK ·
THE MINNEAPOLIS INSTITUTE OF ARTS · MUSEUM OF ART ·
CARNEGIE INSTITUTE · PITTSBURGH · PENNSYLVANIA ·
PHILADELPHIA MUSEUM OF ART · ST. LOUIS ART MUSEUM ·
TOLEDO MUSEUM OF ART · LESSING J. ROSENWALD COLLECTION ·
NATIONAL GALLERY OF ART · WASHINGTON · D.C. · DAVISON ART
CENTER · WESLEYAN UNIVERSITY · MIDDLETOWN · CONNECTICUT ·
STERLING AND FRANCINE CLARK ART INSTITUTE · WILLIAMSTOWN ·
MASSACHUSETTS · THE WORCESTER ART MUSEUM · YALE
UNIVERSITY ART GALLERY · NEW HAVEN · CONNECTICUT

ACKNOWLEDGMENTS

Special recognition is due those who contributed significant assistance to the preparation of the exhibition, and to the research and writing of the catalogue. Elise K. Kenney edited the text and translated the poems. Claire Frierson transcribed Meryon's *Mes Observations*. Marilyn Beckhorn contributed research and managed the vast organizational detail, assisted by Deborah Hoover and Thomas Kren. New translations from French were prepared by Elise Kenney and the author, with the aid of Susan Burke.

Some of the earlier research in France was supported in part by a Museum Professional Fellowship grant by the Smithsonian Institution under the provisions of the National Museum Act (Public Law 91-629), as amended, and the National Endowment for the Arts.

For specific advice and assistance, I am grateful to Harley Preston for several conversations on Meryon, and to Arthur Driver of P. & D. Colnaghi, London, for his help with Harold Wright's notes. Jean Adhémar of the Bibliothèque Nationale, Paris, offered several valuable suggestions for research. At Toledo, William Hutton and Roger Mandle provided valuable assistance, as did Charles Buckley and Nancy Nielson at St. Louis. A few words cannot suffice to thank colleagues in the print collections in the United States who helped locate impressions and assisted in the study of originals. To the lenders go our deepest thanks for cooperating in this undertaking, especially to those who expedited the many arrangements: Leon Arkus, Jacob Bean, Richard S. Field, George Heard Hamilton, Sinclair Hitchings, John W. Ittmann, Harold Joachim, Ann Lockhart, John J. McKendry, Kneeland McNulty, Ruth S. Magurn, R. Peter Mooz, Weston Naef, Louise S. Richards, Timothy Riggs, Andrew Robison, Lessing J. Rosenwald, Barbara Shapiro, Ellen Sharp, and Herdis Teilman. In addition, the many colleagues and friends who gave indispensable advice and help are offered thanks: Daniel Arnheim, Egbert Haverkamp-Begemann, Richard Brettell, Marjorie Benedict Cohn, Michelle DeAngelus, Douglas Druick, Anne Coffin Hanson, Jean Harris, Robert L. Herbert, Dr. James D. Kenney, R. E. Lewis, Edmund P. Pillsbury, Danielle Rice, and Peter Schatborn.

At the Yale University Art Gallery, Fernande Ross and Gale Thompson handled transportation and loan arrangements. Dorothy Hooker and Estelle Miehle helped with administration. Photography was arranged by Denise D'Avella, done by Joseph Szaszfai and Mark Isenberg. Robert M. Soule, Superintendent, supervised installation and shipping arrangements.

We are grateful to Leonard Baskin for designing the catalogue. His love of Meryon and his great sensitivity to the graphic arts have been an asset of the highest order. John Peckham and Harold Hugo of the Meriden Gravure Company arranged the printing. At the Yale University Printing Service, Greer Allen helped and gave his time to every phase of the actual production of the catalogue. Finally, the ultimate debt is to the artist, and to the many admirers in North America who collected his works, without whom this exhibition would not have been possible.

Bradley, 1917 William A. Bradley, "Some Meryon Drawings in the MacGeorge Collection," *Print Collector's Quarterly* VII, (1917) pp. 223-255.

Burty I, 1863 Philippe Burty, "L'Oeuvre de M. Charles Meryon I," *Gazette des Beaux-Arts* XIV, (June 1863) pp. 519-533.

Burty II, 1863 Philippe Burty, "L'Oeuvre de M. Charles Meryon II," *Gazette des Beaux-Arts* XIV, (July 1863) pp. 75-88.

Burty, 1880 Philippe Burty, "Charles Meryon," *La Nouvelle Revue* II, (1880) pp. 115-138.

Burty and Huish, 1879 Philippe Burty and Marcus Huish, *Charles Meryon—Sailor, Engraver, and Etcher. A Memoir and Complete Descriptive Catalogue of his Works*, London, 1879.

Delteil, 1907 Löys Delteil, *Le Peintre-Graveur Illustré: Charles Meryon*, Paris, 1907.

DW, 1924 Löys Delteil and Harold J. L. Wright, *Catalogue Raisonné of the Etchings of Charles Meryon*, New York, 1924.

Grigaut, 1950 Paul L. Grigaut, "Some Unpublished or Little Known Meryon Drawings in the Toledo Museum of Art," *Art Quarterly* XIII, (1950) pp. 228-240.

Grolier Club, N.Y. 1898 *A Catalogue of Etchings and Drawings by Charles Meryon Exhibited at the Grolier Club*, Exhibition catalogue, New York, 1898.

Knoedler, N.Y. 1917 *Etchings and Drawings by Charles Meryon: The B. B. MacGeorge Collection*, Exhibition catalogue, M. Knoedler and Co., New York, 1917.

L. Frits Lugt, *Les Marques de collections des dessins et d'estampes*, Amsterdam, 1921 and *Supplément*, The Hague, 1956.

Paris 1968 Jean Ducros, *Charles Meryon, Officier de Marine, Peintre-Graveur, 1821-1868*, Exhibition catalogue, Musée de la Marine, Paris, 1968-1969.

Rogers, 1963 Millard F. Rogers, Jr., *The Drawings of Charles Meryon*, Toledo Museum of Art Handbook, Toledo, 1963.

Rogers TMN, 1963   Millard F. Rogers, Jr., "The Drawings of Charles Meryon," *Toledo Museum News* VI, no. 2, (1963).

Rutgers 1971   *Meryon's Paris/Piranesi's Rome,* Exhibition catalogue Rutgers University Art Gallery, New Brunswick, 1971.

Williamstown 1966   *French Drawings of the Nineteenth Century,* Exhibition, Sterling and Francine Clark Art Institute, Williamstown, 1966.

A SMALL GROUP OF ARTISTS AND CONNOISSEURS gathered more than 106 years ago at the cemetery of the asylum at Charenton for the burial of Charles Meryon. His death, following insanity, did not command the attention of the press, but a small circle of old friends reverently heard one of their number, Gustave Salicis, commend him to the history of art.[1]

Today we see Meryon as one of the first important artists of any period to devote himself entirely to drawing and printmaking. He is probably the greatest French etcher of any time, and was undoubtedly a unique and compelling talent in a country and century which valued and nurtured many such individuals.

Etching had not been widely used since the seventeenth century in the Netherlands, although in France, Fragonard, Boucher and others had etched in the eighteenth century. In the late 1830s and 1840s the Barbizon artists began to use the medium again.[2] Apart from drawings, Meryon worked in no other medium. For this he was important to the revival of etching as a technique that has captivated artists from Manet and Pissarro to Picasso and Edward Hopper. Philippe Burty, his friend and an important art critic who formed a major collection of his prints and drawings, said that Meryon's work was "absolutely personal. His great originality, which is by no means within the reach of everyone, stems from neither any master nor any school."[3] Meryon's following was small in the strictest sense,[4] but the spirit and vitality of his work still is outstanding in its influence, and its power to command our attention.

Meryon was clearly part of the Paris of his time. He was devoted to the city as the subject matter of his art. He drew and etched numerous landmarks and street scenes in Paris, and published one group of etchings of Paris as a set, *Eaux-Fortes sur Paris*. He also did views of Bourges, although he never fulfilled his idea to publish them as a group. All the major work of his most prolific period, 1850-1855, was concerned with the city. Meryon's contemporary, the poet and critic, Charles Baudelaire, called these prints "the scenery of great cities, . . . a collection of dimension and elegance from a rich agglomeration of men and monuments, the vast charm of a capital aged and growing old in the glories and tribulations of life."[5] For Baudelaire and Victor Hugo, as for Meryon and other French citizens of the mid-nineteenth century, the city, especially Paris, was increasingly regarded as the very seat of civilization. Urban life, now mushrooming at an unprecedented rate, was beginning to be recognized as a fitting subject of art and literature. The vast influx from the provinces filled the oldest parts of Paris, notably the Ile de la Cité and the Left Bank, with new urban lower classes. Meryon lived in these overcrowded, small-scale medieval neighborhoods; his feeling for the value of the old city is infused into each print. In the late 1840s, a few renovations had already occurred to change old Paris, but the stage was set for the massive new works of the Second Empire. Dozens of small streets and alleys, teeming with life, complex warrens still remaining from the late Middle Ages, would be destroyed in the wholesale remodeling of these areas by the new city plans of Baron Haussmann and Louis Napoleon (1853-1869).[6]

Just as Renaissance Italians of the fifteenth century discovered the classical past that surrounded their daily lives, so the French of the mid-nineteenth century found their medieval heritage. Gothic Revival was a clear fact by the 1840s in France, although there was also a rising interest in every aspect of the history of art and archaeology of the Middle Ages.[7] By 1845, one of the leading figures of the Gothic Revival, Eugène-Emmanuel Viollet-le-Duc (1814-1879) was flatly calling Gothic the national style of France.[8]

Everywhere in France, people became concerned with the culture of their past, particularly that of the Middle Ages. Delaborde's great series on the French cathedrals, *Les Monuments de la France*, appeared from 1818 to 1836. Baron Taylor began his historical picture books in 1820, *Voyages pittoresques et romantiques dans l'ancienne France*, which continued until 1878. The first half of the century saw the founding of the great historical societies: the *Société Nationale des Antiquaires de France* (1814), and the *Société Française d'Archéologie pour la Conservation des Monuments Historiques* (1834). An official government organization, the *Commission pour la Conservation des Monuments Historiques*, followed shortly in 1837, charged with the survey, restoration and supervision of medieval monuments. The Commission's first project was to hire Viollet-le-Duc to restore the Romanesque church at Vézelay (1840-1845). In 1843-1845, the Commission hired him to begin restorations on the Cathedral of Notre-Dame in Paris, no doubt a direct result of the interest generated by Victor Hugo's book of the same name.[9] By 1851, the Commission had even set out to make photographic records of the major monuments.[10]

Historical consciousness of all kinds was rising, closely connected to the appreciation of Gothic architecture. Victor Hugo's role cannot be overestimated here; his *Notre-Dame de Paris*, first published in 1831, was the wellspring of a movement that glorified the history of France, the city of Paris and the Cathedral. Church and city were each celebrated and raised together to the status of national treasures. The most influential voice of this popular movement which sought to honor and preserve Paris belonged to Victor Hugo. It was followed soon after by historians, cartographers, philosophers, archaeologists and the ascendant middle class.

It is against this background of new urbanism and growing antiquarianism that we can best understand the subjects of Meryon's prints and drawings. He loved the cityscape itself, and his finest works are certainly those of Paris and Bourges. They are a preservationist's plea for urban heritage, done with an antiquarian's fixation on detail. Meryon's letters reveal his sharp sense of recording and his devotion to the passing appearances of the city. Even modest but authentic medieval detail caught his eye; at Bourges, he wrote to Burty, "I found . . . in the streets, on the outside of the houses, most curious effects of construction, principally of a kind which is rapidly disappearing because it is not counted of sufficient importance to be either restored or preserved."[11]

Meryon became one of the first to portray a city in a personal manner. The many prints of urban subjects made in France in the first half of the nineteenth century

2

were essentially conservative, close to the tradition of cartographic views. The results were based on seventeenth and eighteenth century view-formulae (one would think of Callot or Canaletto) with vast forespaces, some modicum of descriptive detail and panoramic intention. Two tiny views of the Morgue (Cats. 112 and 113) illustrate the point, with their conflict of small size and grand pretension, and discordant shifts in scale.[12] However, Meryon's city etchings attempt a view analogous to photography in format. Seldom does he undertake the expansive panoramic view of earlier popularity, as he did in *Le Pont-au-Change* (DW 34), *L'Abside de Notre-Dame* (DW 38) and the *Collège Henri IV* (DW 43). Most of his urban subjects are more specific, such as *Tourelle de la Rue de la Tixéranderie* (DW 29); they are controlled in their limits of breadth, depth and scale as if seen through the lens of a camera. More than the camera's eye could see, though, are the refined tension and compression of spaces, and the great subtlety with which Meryon controls perspective to avoid obvious distortion. Here Meryon is the cataloguer of medieval architectural genre, the portraitist of the tense, forbidding city that contains its harried masses. Like Victor Hugo, Meryon treasured the city, sought to protect it, and was conscious of the urban setting as a major condition of life in his times. Meryon thought to improve city life in two etched poems, *La Loi Lunaire* and *La Loi Solaire* (DW 91 and 93), by creating fanciful decrees for the improvement of the urban resident's life, setting aside free space for light and sun. Paris already had a tradition as a sophisticated urban center; but Meryon's time brought a social, political and artistic consciousness of both the city and its residents.

Meryon's naval training equipped him with a meticulous style of drawing of the type that a military draughtsman of the time required. It stressed faithful rendering and accurate description at the expense of expressionistic values; this kind of drawing is perhaps closer to the sciences of topography, cartography, and surveying than to traditional landscape art.[13] Such qualities, along with his own mania for exactitude, comprise some of the major characteristics of his art. This penchant may explain his attraction to photography, which probably occurred about 1849-1850, a time when photography was undergoing significant developments in Paris. The whole concept of Meryon's spaces owes something to photography and optics, although the dramatic condensation is certainly his own. From the camera too, comes the sharpness of detail, over-contrast of tonal qualities and general sense of light.

In his first original works, *Le Petit Pont* (DW 24) and *L'Arche du Pont Notre-Dame* (DW 25), the initial drawings were made with the aid of a "chambre claire," as Meryon called it. This was probably a camera lucida or similar device, by which the image of a scene could be projected onto paper, or traced.[14] But it did not suffice, and in each case considerable changes were made in subsequent drawings. Certain architectural elements were enlarged out of scale for emphasis, or perspective was subtly shifted to enhance various aspects of the subject. What remained from the camera was the mise-en-scène, a basic format for the total arrangement. Within the edges of the plate is a complete world, not just of architecture, space and line, but of human detail and emotion. Not the discretely populated Rome of Piranesi or the Venice of Canaletto, this is a thriving metropolitan Paris jammed with humanity. Only Bourges, a smaller country town, is less congested for Meryon. Vast throngs pour over the bridges in *La Tour de l'Horloge* (DW 28), *Le Pont-au-Change* (DW 34), and *L'Abside de Notre-Dame* (DW 38), or gather ominously in *La Morgue* (DW 36). Dark birds threaten in *Le Stryge* (DW 23) or mass in the skies of a later state of *Le Pont-au-Change* (Cat. 58), suggesting Edgar Allen Poe. Often where thin, mannered figures appear there is an unsettling urgency, as in *La Morgue* (DW 36), where rushing policemen, corpse-bearers and a bereaved woman contrast with the angry crowd. Or, as in *Le Pont-au-Change* (DW 34), open and airy in view, we find a balloon rising as if to offset and balance a small man foundering in the river below. This is a combination of innocent setting and foreboding detail to delight an Alfred Hitchcock.

The tense line, dark shadows and strange staffage are elements that distinguish Meryon's work, yet one cannot help regarding them as signs of his mental illness. The latter etchings demonstrate this more clearly with the allegorical and fantastic figures that appear in the skies of *Tourelle, Rue de l'Ecole de Médecine* (Cat. 72), and *Le Ministère de la Marine* (DW 45), or that populate fore- and backgrounds in *Collège Henri IV* (DW 43). Burty found these "scènes fantastiques" signs of insanity and intimated his disapproval.[15] We are more generous today, thinking of them as romantic visions, recalling Hieronymous Bosch and other artists of late Gothic times. Meryon is a fascinating enigma, romantic in his visions, obsessions and fantasies, yet realistic in his attachment to observable nature and to the subjects of his social environment.

In this exhibition we concentrate on the three major phases of Meryon's art: the Views of Paris, Views of Bourges, and Views of Oceania and New Zealand. Some incidental works accompany these, such as poems meant to accompany the images, portraits, and some miscellany. Preparatory drawings are shown in direct conjunction with fine impressions of the prints in their significant states to underscore the artist's development and working method. A few additional drawings serve to illuminate differing aspects of Meryon's work, as does the inclusion of two of the artist's original copper plates. The emphasis here is also directed to connoisseurship of Meryon's prints, particularly to the subtle choices of papers, delicate tones of ink color, differences in inking and wiping of the plate, and varying resultant effects in the different impressions. The viewer is invited, even encouraged, to choose and compare impressions of these etchings and to concentrate on the individual works of art themselves. Almost every impression of an etching printed by Meryon himself is slightly different from the next. It is hoped that the viewer will realize both the intricacy and the extraordinary quality of Meryon's prints and drawings as unique works of art.

Charles Meryon was born in Paris on November 23, 1821.[16] His mother was

Pierre-Narcisse Chaspoux (1793-1838), a dancer in the Paris Opera who used Narcisse Gentil as her stage name.[17] Charles Lewis Meryon (1783-1877), an English physician, was his father. Born in France of Huguenot parents, he emigrated to England when he was a child and was a naturalized British citizen, educated at Oxford.[18]

Charles Meryon was an illegitimate child, a fact that haunted him throughout his life. He was not acknowledged by his father until he was three years of age, and only then because of his mother's imploring, pitiful letters; his father's full acceptance would wait until 1864.[19] In 1826, under the name "Gentil," he entered school at the Pension Savary at Passy where Dr. Meryon paid his expenses.[20] Three years later he was baptized a Protestant. During his fourteenth year, he travelled along the southern coast of France and in parts of Italy, possibly with his mother; he was with his father in Marseilles and spent the winter in Florence. When he was nearly fifteen years of age, he vacationed with the Réaume family at Conches. We know that he was interested in art at that age, for some years later he sent the family a drawing done that summer.[21]

The family name Meryon was first used by Charles when he entered the naval school at Brest in 1837.[22] The following year his mother died in a state of insanity, according to Burty.[23] Thereafter he began a series of sea voyages that spanned the next seven years. Each voyage began from Toulon; on October 15, 1839 he sailed on the *Alger* and then on the *Montebello* in 1840 to Algiers, Tunisia, Smyrna (Izmir), Athens, Argos and Tiryns. During this trip he was promoted to first class, and drew both the frieze inside the Hephaisteion and the Choragic Monument to Lysicrates in Athens (then in the courtyard of the French Capuchin Convent), a subject to which he would return in later years (*DW* 61).[24] At Toulon, in this same year, he began formal lessons in watercolor with the painter Victor Courdouan (1810-1893), about whom little is known.[25] The third voyage, which lasted four years, was to the Pacific on the corvette *Rhin*, departing August 15, 1842.[26] The ship sailed to Brazil; around Cape Horn to Akaroa, Banks Peninsula, New Zealand (January 1843); Sydney, Australia to Valparaiso; Tahiti and again to New Zealand, leaving in April 1846 to return by way of St. Helena and Gibraltar to Toulon. The prospect must have excited Meryon, for he wrote to his father that he intended to "observe, draw, and paint."[27] This marks Meryon's first period of serious artistic activity, and provided the source for his etchings of 1863-1866 (*DW* 63-72).

Meryon returned to Paris on leave-of-absence from the Navy in 1846.[28] In November he wrote to his father of his "grande décision" to devote himself to art as a vocation.[29] He began art lessons with Charles François Philippe (d. 1867), a minor pupil of Jacques-Louis David, who was employed by the War Ministry. He required Meryon to draw from casts of ancient sculptures in the prevailing academic tradition.[30] Settling in Paris, Meryon rented a studio in the rue Hautefeuille.[31] In 1847, Meryon travelled to Rouen, Dieppe, Brighton, and London where he visited his half-sister, (Eugénie Meryon) Mrs. Broadwood. He wrote to his old shipmate Foley of his liking for London clubs, the high prices paid there for works of art, and described other details of the trip. Returning to Paris by way of Belgium, he saw Ostende, Bruges, Ghent, Antwerp, and Brussels, and throughout the trip he discussed his great interest in architecture and painting in the letters to Foley.[32] Meryon resigned from the Navy in July 1848, and failed in a complicated attempt to obtain a position in the Cartographic Office of the Navy.[33] The Revolution of that spring seems to have thrilled him, and his letters to his father and to Foley voice his favor and hope for the new Republic.[34] At the same time he completed a highly finished preliminary drawing for a projected painting of the *Assassination of Marion Du Frêne*, a French Naval captain killed by natives in New Zealand in 1772. This drawing (now in the Alexander Turnbull Library, Wellington, N.Z.) was accepted and exhibited in the Salon of 1848 (No. 3283), and is generally taken to be the key point in his artistic career because it permitted him to break away from his teacher, M. Philippe, and led to his acquaintance with Eugène Bléry, a minor artist who made fine landscape etchings.[35] Philippe Burty reports that while painting the *Assassination of Marion Du Frêne*, Meryon discovered that he was colorblind.[36] As early as 1841, Meryon knew that he had trouble with perception of colors, and in 1846, he admitted that he preferred prints with fine tonal gradations as a result of this condition.[37] Daltonism implied an end to his career in painting, considered by many, then as now, the most important art form. At the Salon of 1848, Meryon met Bléry and discovered etching as an alternative to painting. From December 1848 to July 1849, Meryon lived and worked with Bléry at his home on Place Saint-André-des-Arts.[38] His first prints (*DW* 1-16) were made under Bléry's tutelage, and all were copies after etchings by older masters: Karel Dujardin (Dutch, ca. 1622-1678), Salvator Rosa (Italian, 1615-1673), Adriaen van de Velde (Dutch, 1636-1672), J. P. de Loutherbourg (French, 1740-1812), and Reynier Nooms, called Zeeman (Dutch, ca. 1623-before 1667). With Bléry, Meryon learned the art and technique of etching, a medium not widely used by artists of the time.[39] Yet it was Zeeman's prints with their crisp detail that impressed him most, especially the Parisian subjects.[40]

In the fall of 1848 Meryon travelled to Normandy and to Bourges.[41] There is little other documentary information about Meryon after this time. We do know that he moved to 26, rue Neuve Saint-Etienne-du-Mont by July 1849,[42] and later that same year the great set, *Eaux-Fortes sur Paris*, was begun; this suite is still considered his finest work. The five years that followed were the artist's most active and productive, with only the faintest glimmerings of public recognition. His first original work, *Le Petit Pont* (*DW* 24), was completed and accepted in the Salon of 1850. The Salon of 1852 saw *Saint-Etienne-du-Mont* (*DW* 30) exhibited; in 1853, the Salon jury accepted *La Pompe Notre-Dame* (*DW* 31) but rejected *La Galerie Notre-Dame* (*DW* 26) and *Rue des Toiles à Bourges* (*DW* 55). *La Pompe Notre-Dame* was exhibited in the Salon of 1855, along with *L'Abside de Notre-Dame* (*DW* 38).

Jules Niel (d. 1872), librarian at the Ministry of the Interior, was one of the first to collect Meryon's work seriously. He had met Meryon by 1854 and arranged for the Ministry to purchase sets of prints for its library.[43] Despite Niel's patronage, Meryon was not doing well financially. Moreover, Meryon's mental state, always delicate, now became so serious that his old shipmate Foley, a medical student at the time, wrote to Dr. Meryon in London (December 12, 1855), informing him that Charles was sick and needed help.[44] This was the beginning of the artist's long psychiatric history, which lasted until his death in the asylum at Charenton.[45]

In October 1856 Niel was visited by the savants Edmond and Jules Goncourt, who came to admire his Meryon collection. Their impressions, written in a private journal, gave an excellent contemporary appraisal of the fine quality of Meryon's work. The Goncourt brothers clearly appreciated the sense of bygone times and mystery in the etchings, and provide some indication of the increasing progress of the artist's mental deterioration:

> It seems as though a hand of the past has held the engraver's
> needle and that more than the very stonework of old Paris has been
> brought to these sheets of paper. Indeed, in his images, one could
> say some of the soul of the old city had been revived. It is as
> though magical reminiscence of old quarters, foundering oftentimes
> as in a dream, troubles the mind of a clairvoyant conscious of
> perspective—the poet-artist—who has Lunacy and wretchedness
> seated nearby on his bench. . . .
> Poor unhappy madman, during the clear moments beyond his
> lunacy, takes endless walks to capture the picturesque strangeness
> of shadows in the great cities.[46]

Despite gradual mental and physical decline, Meryon started working on the view of *San Francisco* (*DW 73*), painstakingly based on or copied from daguerreotype views taken on the site. Execution of this unusually large plate took almost a year and was not completed until early 1857; Meryon, his mind troubled, was unable and unwilling to work with the sureness and ease of touch seen in the earlier etchings.

Although words of praise and recognition followed after this time, Meryon's artistic faculties generally had begun to falter as his mental problems grew more acute. He received a commission from the Duc d'Arenberg to make a series of etchings of the park around his estate at Enghien near Brussels in the spring of 1857. Just before Meryon travelled there later that summer, his finances were so poor that his friends organized a private lottery on his behalf.[47] During his stay until March 1858, nothing came of either the etchings or some of his experiments with photography, as his mental instability grew.[48] He moved to a new flat on his return to Paris, but was now in low spirits. Burty reported that Meryon dug up his garden looking for corpses, and that Auguste Delâtre, the printer, often cared for him.[49] In the spring his friends seem to have called on him frequently. On one such occasion, May 11, 1858, Leopold Flameng drew him sitting up in bed, staring into space (Fig. 1).[50] The following morning he was taken by the police to the asylum at Charenton, where he was described as "suffering from melancholy madness, complicated by delusion."[51]

While Meryon was at Charenton, the first critical review of his work was published by Baudelaire in his review of the Salon of 1859:

> A few years ago, a forceful and unique man, a naval officer, it is said, had begun a series of etched studies done from some of the most picturesque vantage points of Paris. Because of the sharpness, delicacy and certainty of his design, M. Meryon brought to mind some old and excellent etchers. I have rarely seen the natural solemnity of an immense city depicted with more poetry. The majesty of piled up masonry, the bell towers pointing a finger to the sky, the obelisks of industry vomiting their coalitions against the heavens, the marvelous scaffolding, in a day when beauty is so paradoxical, that imposes its structure on the substantial main portion of the architecture while monuments are being repaired, the tumultuous sky wrought up by anger and bitterness, the depth of the perspective augmented by contemplation of all dramas confined therein—none of these complex elements that compose the mournful and glorious scenery of civilization are overlooked. If Victor Hugo had seen these excellent prints, he would have been content. He would have found worthily represented his:
>
> > Mournful Isis, shrouded by a veil.
> > Spider-well of immense canvas
> > Where nations are caught!
> > Spring to tormented urns!
> > Breast, ceaselessly overflowing
> > Where generations come
> > To be nourished from an idea!
> >
> > . . . .
> > City that a storm has darkened!
>
> But a cruel demon has touched M. Meryon's brain; a mysterious delirium has confounded his faculties which seem both substantial and brilliant. His nascent glory and his work have been interrupted suddenly. And since then, we are eagerly awaiting reassuring news about this unique officer who has become a masterful artist over-night and who said goodbye to the solemn adventures of the ocean to depict the dark majesty of the most restless of capitals.[52]

Victor Hugo soon saw Meryon's prints, for some impressions were sent to the author, then in exile in Guernsey. Hugo replied to Baudelaire (April 29, 1860):

Since you know M. Meryon, tell him that his splendid etchings have dazzled me. Without color—nothing but shade and light, chiaroscuro all alone and entrusted to itself: there is the challenge of etching. M. Meryon resolves it magisterially. What he does is superb. His plates live, sparkle and think. He deserves the deep and luminous page that he has inspired in you.[53]

Three years later, other generous comments of Victor Hugo were published by Burty:

These etchings are magnificent things. We must not allow this splendid imagination to be defeated in the struggle in which it is engaged with the Infinite whether studying the Ocean or Paris. Strengthen him with all possible encouragement. The breath of immensity passes through all his works, and makes his etchings more than pictures—visions.[54]

There is evidence that he was sent an impression of *La Pompe Notre-Dame* (*DW* 31) in 1855, and that he knew Meryon's work from originals.
Meryon met Baudelaire sometime in late 1859, presumably after he was released from the asylum in August. He took a room at rue Duperré and, in poor finances once again, he wrote for help to the Minister of State in charge of the Arts, receiving a small amount.[55] This was hardly enough to sustain him, and his affairs undoubtedly deteriorated. In 1860, Baudelaire suggested to the publisher Poulet-Malassis that he should edit and release a new printing of the *Eaux-Fortes sur Paris*, adding that "Meryon does not know how to sell and he cannot find a publisher. His work will sell easily."[56] Somehow, at this same time, Baudelaire reported that he was to do texts to accompany the etchings, "a dozen small poems or sonnets," or "poetic reveries written in prose."[57] Baudelaire wrote that it was:

a chance to write some musings of ten lines, or twenty to thirty lines about handsome prints, philosophic dreams of a strolling Parisian. But M. Meryon has interfered; he will not hear of such a thing. It must say: at the right this can be seen; at the left, that can be seen. I must search for notations among the booksellers' stalls. I must go to the Hôtel de Ville to make inquiries about the exact date of the demolitions. M. Meryon speaks, his eyes on the ceiling, without listening to any observations.[58]

In 1861 Delâtre printed the plates after retouching by the artist, but Baudelaire's lines never appeared. Although this edition of the *Eaux-Fortes sur Paris* was commercially produced, it seems that Meryon still had his small wooden printing press at his studio and that his work went on. Burty believes this was Meryon's weakest period due to mental instability, and justifiably so.[59] Commissions from friends and the proposed set of etchings of subjects from the Pacific voyage of twenty years earlier comprised his work at this time; however, it lacked the freshness of inspiration and vitality of the *Eaux-Fortes sur Paris*. He exhibited two prints, *Le Grand Châtelet* (DW 52) and *Tourelle, Rue de l'Ecole de Médecine* (DW 41) at the International Exhibition of 1862 in London.[60] Prints of the *Voyage à la Nouvelle Zélande* were reputed to sell for 1000 francs,[61] and Meryon's own collection went on the auction block, drawing good, but not high, prices.[62]

Four prints were accepted in the Salon of 1863: these are *Tourelle, Rue de l'Ecole de Médecine* (DW 41), *La Rue des Chantres* (DW 42), *Le Grand Châtelet* (DW 52), and *Nouvelle-Calédonie: Grande Case Indigène* ... (DW 67).[63] That same year saw the publication of Burty's catalogue of Meryon's work in the prestigious *Gazette des Beaux-Arts*. The catalogue was based on conversations and correspondence with Meryon, who wrote out meticulous responses to it. This unpublished document, *Mes Observations*, is now at the Toledo Museum of Art.

He also exhibited in the Salons of 1864, 1865, 1866 and 1867: in 1864, *L'Arche du Pont Notre-Dame* (DW 25), *Océanie, Ilots à Uvea: Pêche aux Palmes* (DW 68), *Presqu'île de Banks, Pointe des Charbonniers* (DW 69); in 1865, *Greniers Indigènes* ... *à Akaroa* (DW 70); in 1867, *Petite Colonie Française à Akaroa* (DW 71). Yet this popular success arrived at the least prolific and most troubled time of his life. Only two prints done at this time merit special attention. The first, *Le Ministère de la Marine* (DW 45), was made for publication by *La Société des Aquafortistes* (August 1865); the second came through Burty's intercession with the Comte de Nieuwerkerke, Director General of the Imperial Museums.[64] It was a commission for Meryon to etch a copy after Zeeman's painting of the *Old Louvre* (DW 53) for the Chalcographie du Louvre, formally published in 1866 and exhibited in the Salon of that year.

On October 12, 1866, Meryon was taken to Charenton for the second and last time.[65] His creative energies were lost as his psychiatric problems deepened. His last letters are garbled, guilt-ridden ravings.[66] He died in February 1868, of exhaustion and starvation, "believing himself to be Christ held captive by the Pharisees, and being unwilling to wrong the feeble and outcast by taking their food."[67]

He was a gentle person, extremely oversensitive and humble, a deeply introspective artist who had created and preserved on paper a special vision that still has power to affect us today. It is a fragile old world of medieval streets and civic pride, destroyed and built by the Second Empire. The remarkable lucidity of his images, so striking in their faithfulness to nature, are filled with mystery and tension. This heightened intensity is combined with deep over-contrasts of light and shadow to portray an immense city in which tiny incidental dramas are played out amidst masses of humans. It is a world of unseen forces, fascinating and mystical; a spirit that would continue later in the art of Bresdin, Redon and Ensor, and extend into the works of the Surrealists in our century.

JAMES D. BURKE

1. *Burty and Huish*, 1879, pp. 27-28.   2. The best discussion of the history of etching in France before Meryon's time, and a description of the medium, is found in Arthur M. Hind, *A History of Engraving and Etching, from the 15th Century to the year 1914*, New York, 1923.   3. *Burty I*, 1863, pp. 519-533 and *Burty II*, 1863, pp. 75-88. A brief discussion of Burty's role as a critic is in Gabriel P. Weisberg, "Philippe Burty—A Notable Critic of the Nineteenth Century," *Apollo* XCI, (April 1970) pp. 296-300.   4. He had only one known student, Gabrielle Niel (ca. 1840—after 1866), the daughter of his friend and patron, Jules Niel. See Henri Beraldi, *Les Graveurs du XIXᵉ Siècle*, 12 vols., Paris, 1885-1892, X, pp. 197-198. Only Maxime Lalanne (1827-1886) can be called a close follower, particularly in his etching, *Rue des Marmousets, Vieux Paris*, 1863 (Beraldi I). In the year of its publication, this etching was immediately seen as deriving from Meryon by Burty in his review of *"La Société des Aquafortistes,"* Gazette des Beaux-Arts XIV, (February 1863) p. 192 and Janine Bailly-Herzberg, *L'Eau-forte de Peintre au Dix-Neuvième Siècle: La Société des Aquafortistes 1862-1867*, 2 vols., Paris, 1972, I, p. 58, no. 15, reproduced.   5. Y. G. Le Dantec, ed., *Baudelaire, Oeuvres Complètes*, Paris, 1961, pp. 1083-1084. Quoted from Baudelaire's review of the Salon of 1859.   6. Howard Saalman, *Haussmann: Paris Transformed*, New York, 1971. An excellent critical overview and bibliography of Second Empire city planning. It includes a brief history of Paris as a city. For a popular account of the politics of the time, see J. and B. Chapman, *The Life and Times of Baron Haussmann—Paris in the Second Empire*, London, 1957.   7. The basic source on Gothic Revivals in Europe and their differing qualities is Agnes Addison, *Romanticism and the Gothic Revival*, New York, 1938.
8. Eugène-Emmanuel Viollet-le-Duc, "L'Art national et l'art étranger," *Annales Archaeologiques* II, (1845) pp. 305-309; idem, "Du style gothique au XIXᵉ siècle," ibid., IV, (1846) pp. 333-353.   9. *Eugène Viollet-le-Duc (1814-1879)*, Exhibition catalogue, Caisse Nationale des Monuments Historiques, Paris, 1965, pp. 39-68. The restorations of Notre-Dame are discussed by Marcel Aubert, *La Cathédrale de Note-Dame de Paris: notice historique et archéologique*, Paris, 1945. A brief and thoughtful account of Viollet-le-Duc's importance can be found in Nikolaus Pevsner, *Ruskin and Viollet-le-Duc: Englishness and Frenchness in the Appreciation of Gothic Architecture*, London, 1969. Viollet-le-Duc and Meryon were acquainted; for the architect visited him while Meryon was hospitalized at Charenton in 1858 and gave him a drawing of the ruins of the Château of Pierrefonds. The drawing is now at the Toledo Museum of Art (pencil, 172 x 248 mm., 23.3116); it was the basis for Meryon's etching of the château done that year (*DW* 59).   10. Robert Sobieszek and André Jammes, *French Primitive Photography*, Exhibition catalogue, Philadelphia Museum of Art, Philadelphia, 1969.   11. *Burty and Huish*, 1879, p. 10. Meryon's own antiquarianism is evident in his copies of 17th and 18th century prints of Paris (*DW* 46-48 and *DW* 50-52), his two plates of Chenonceaux, (*DW* 57 and 58), one of the apse of Saint Martin-sur-Renelle (*DW* 60), and several portraits of historical figures and contemporary antiquarians (*DW* 76-86). In addition, Meryon made an etched copy of a late Gothic manuscript illumination for Jules Niel (*DW* 94). The copper plate for this still exists at the St. Louis Art Museum.   12. Examples of the topographically-oriented view and more typical format of the period are found in Edmond Texier, *Tableau de Paris*, Paris, 1852; this work also contains an enormous amount of useful visual information on contemporary city life.   13. Meryon was not a proponent of realism in the sense of Courbet, Manet and the Impressionists, as recently defined in Linda Nochlin, *Realism*, Baltimore, 1971. Instead, he was involved with realism in a much broader sense and is an almost classic example of what Ackerman terms "scientific realism." See Gerald Ackerman, *Jean-Léon Gérôme (1824-1904)*. Exhibition catalogue, Dayton Art Institute, Dayton, 1972-1973, p. 14; and also Ackerman's review of Linda Nochlin, *"Realism,"* Art Bulletin LV, (September 1973) pp. 466-469.   14. See Cat. 14 and Cat. 20. The camera lucida is discussed and illustrated in Helmut and Allison Gernsheim, *The History of Photography, 1685-1914*, New York, 1969, p. 29, pl. 14.   15. *Burty*, 1880, pp. 133-134. For an opposing view on the value of these visions see Fritz Novotny, *Painting and Sculpture in Europe, 1780-1850*, Baltimore, 1960, pp. 98-100.   16. *Burty I*, 1863, p. 520.   17. Meryon himself was to suggest later that his mother was of Spanish origin, (see *Burty*, 1880, p. 115). She has been convincingly traced as French; she was recorded by her stage name on the rolls of the Academy of Music at Paris in 1807 and 1814 according to Wolfgang Drost, "Documents Nouveaux sur l'Oeuvre et la Vie de Charles Meryon," *Gazette des Beaux-Arts* LXIII, (April 1964) p. 242, note 6.   18. Drost, 1964, "Documents Nouveaux," p. 242, note 11. Dr. Charles Lewis Meryon is also to be remembered as secretary-physician-companion to Lady Hester Stanhope; he is the author of *Memoirs of the Lady Hester Stanhope, as related by herself in conversation with her Physician*, London, 1845.   19. In 1865, the artist suggested that Dr. Meryon was not his father in a letter, dated May 29, 1865, to Léon Delaunay, *Nouvelles Archives de l'Art Français* V, (1877) pp.

380-395; this attitude no doubt conditioned by his mental state at the time. However, the subject of his own illegitimacy was of lifelong concern to Meryon who had written his father as early as 1840 to beg for recognition; see *Paris 1968*, nos. 287 and 343, and Drost, 1964, "Documents Nouveaux," p. 243, note 19. 20. Delaunay, 1877, *Archives*, p. 393. Meryon used this name throughout his school days, and his father was accustomed to it sufficiently to annotate one letter "C. Gentil 4 Jan. 1845." See *Paris 1968*, no. 353 and *Burty*, 1880, p. 116. 21. For details of his childhood, see *Paris 1968*, nos. 298, 305, and 315; *Burty*, 1880, p. 116 and Delaunay, 1877, *Archives*, p. 389. 22. *Burty I*, 1863, p. 520, and *Burty and Huish*, 1879, pp. 2-3. These reports state that Meryon did not discover his own illegitimacy until 1837, and that this circumstance came as a great shock. 23. *Burty*, 1880, p. 121, note 1. *Paris 1968*, no. 288 states that he had a sister Fannie (Chaspoux), possibly by a different father. In a letter to his father dated November 7, 1838, Meryon says that Fannie has informed him of their mother's death. In the same letter, Charles asks to be remembered to Dr. Meryon's two other children, Jean and Eugénie, and to Madame Meryon; ibid., no. 316. 24. *Burty*, 1880, p. 117. This is mistakenly called the Temple of Theseus in the nineteenth century. 25. *Burty I*, 1863, p. 520; Delaunay, 1877, *Archives*, p. 382; *Paris 1968*, nos. 346 and 513. 26. For a complete itinerary, see Jean Vallery-Radot, "Quand Meryon était Marin," *Gazette des Beaux-Arts* LVII, (May-June 1961) pp. 358-368. 27. *Paris 1968*, no. 348. 28. *Burty I*, 1863, p. 521. 29. *Paris 1968*, no. 366. 30. *Burty*, 1880, pp. 121-122; *Paris 1968*, no. 368. 31. *Burty*, 1880, p. 121; *Paris 1968*, no. 398. 32. *Paris 1968*, nos. 370-383. 33. Ibid., no. 397. 34. Ibid., nos. 384-396. 35. *Burty I*, 1863, p. 521; Aglaus Bouvenne, *Notes et Souvenirs sur Charles Meryon*, Paris, 1883, p. 12; *Paris 1968*, no. 800, reproduced. 36. *Burty I*, 1863, p. 522. 37. See letters to his father, of November 6, 1841 and December 27, 1846 in *Paris 1968*, nos. 341 and 367 respectively. To what extent he was colorblind is not evident. Dalton himself had trouble distinguishing between pinks, light blues and light greens, but could see yellows correctly. Whether Meryon could distinguish between the fine green and blue tints of his etching papers is not clear, although he could certainly see japan and buff papers. John Fulton, ed., *A Textbook of Physiology*, 16th ed., Philadelphia, 1949, pp. 457-459. 38. *Paris 1968*, no. 398. 39. The artist's thanks to his teacher are recorded in his etched verses to Bléry, 1854 (*DW* 88 and 89). 40. As a landscape painter, Zeeman leaned more toward topographical description than many of his contemporaries, except possibly in the case of his marines. For further information, see Wolfgang Stechow, *Dutch Landscape Painting of the Seventeenth Century*, London, 1966, pp. 122-123, 159 and 182. 41. Drost, 1964, "Documents Nouveaux," p. 239, note 58; *Burty*, 1880, p. 122, and *Paris 1968*, no. 400. 42. *Paris 1968*, no. 405. 43. Niel's biography is found in Frits Lugt, *Les Marques de collections de dessins et d'estampes*, I, Amsterdam, 1921, no. 1944. 44. Adele Holcomb, "Le Stryge de Notre-Dame: Some Aspects of Meryon's Symbolism," *Art Journal* XXXI, no. 2, (1971-1972) p. 155 and p. 157, note 22. Foley states that Meryon had an inflammation of the sexual organs which he said "contributed to ruining the sanity of my unfortunate friend." Foley's testimony has been needlessly questioned in *Paris 1968*, nos. 355 and 423. 45. Two interesting modern psychiatric opinions on Meryon and his work are: F. Panse, "Persönlichkeit, Werk und Psychose Charles Meryons," *Archiv für Psychitrie und Zeitschrift Neurologie* CLXXXVII, (1951) pp. 205-230, and Lars-Ingemar Lundström, "Charles Meryon (1821-1867[*sic*]), Peintre-Graveur Schizophrène," *Acta Psychiatrica Scandinavica—Supplementum 40*, Suppl. 180, (1964) pp. 159-165. 46. Edmond and Jules Goncourt, *Journal des Goncourt, mémoires de la vie littéraire*, I, Paris, 1887-1888, pp. 147-148. 47. *Paris 1968*, no. 437. 48. *Burty*, 1880, p. 130. 49. *Burty*, 1880, pp. 131-132, and *Paris 1968*, no. 438. 50. *Burty*, 1880, p. 131, and *Paris 1968*, no. 442. The scene is described in *Burty and Huish*, 1879, p. 29: "Flameng . . . came with a drawing-board . . . and some black crayons . . . and although Meryon did not lend himself to it, he drew a portrait full of character. Meryon . . . is half sitting upon a little iron bed . . . the face, with features sharp and emaciated by the fasting which he voluntarily imposed on himself, has the marks of madness and irony. When this drawing was finished Meryon asked to see it. He jumped out of bed and attempted to tear it to pieces. Flameng fled, upsetting his chair in his flight." 51. *Burty*, 1880, p. 132; Delaunay, 1877, *Archives*, p. 384; *Burty and Huish*, 1879, p. 19. 52. See note 5. 53. Jacques Crépet, ed., *Charles Baudelaire, Etude biographique d'Eugène Crépet*, Paris, 1919, p. 378. 54. *Burty I*, 1863, p. 522. Meryon's name is frequently mentioned in the correspondence between the two writers, Burty and Hugo, published recently by Pierre Georgel, "Le romanticisme des années 1860 [*sic*]: Correspondance Victor Hugo—Philippe Burty," *Revue de l'Art* 20, (1973) pp. 37-64, nos. 1, 3, 5, 11-13, 19-21, and summary, p. 61. 55. *Burty*, 1880, p. 131 and *Paris 1968*, nos. 444-447. 56. Letter of March 9, 1860, see F. F. Gautier and Y. G. Le Dantec, *Oeuvres complètes de Charles*

Baudelaire. Correspondance I: 1841-1863, Paris, 1933, p. 311.   57. Letter of Baudelaire to Poulet-Malassis, March or April 1860, ibid., p. 315.   58. Letter to Poulet-Malassis of February 16, 1860: Eugène Crépet, ed., *Charles Baudelaire, Oeuvres Posthumes et correspondances inédites,* Paris, 1887, p. 198. Baudelaire's other letters concerning Meryon are in Eugène Crépet, ibid., p. 193; Eugène and Jacques Crépet, 1919, *Etude biographique,* pp. 398-399; F. F. Gautier and Y. G. Le Dantec, 1933, *Oeuvres complètes,* pp. 237, 312 and 315; and Léon Cellier, *Baudelaire et Hugo,* Paris, 1970, p. 134.   59. *Burty,* 1880, pp. 133-134.   60. *Paris 1968,* no. 453. The first appreciation of Meryon in English was published two years later by Philip Hamerton, "Modern Etching in France," *The Fine Arts Quarterly Review* II, (January-May 1864) pp. 68-110.   61. *Paris* 1968, no. 451. 62. Charles Baudelaire, 1862, in "Peintres et aquafortistes," in Y. G. Le Dantec, 1961, *Baudelaire,* p. 1148. 63. *Burty II,* 1863, p. 512, no. 4.   64. *Paris 1968,* no. 430.   65. *Burty,* 1880, p. 137.   66. A number of Meryon's late letters are preserved in an album of his correspondence at Toledo, as yet unpublished. The most striking of these is an undated sheet that begins: "Le cri s'outre-tombe! Silence! Oui, je suis l'ange des 12 Fatalités et du sombre Esprit invisible. . . ."   67. *Burty and Huish,* 1879, p. 27; *Burty,* 1880, p. 137-138.

SOME THOUGHTS ON MERYON AND FRENCH PRINTMAKING IN THE NINETEENTH CENTURY   Most standard histories of printmaking suggest that creative etching in France was all but eclipsed for almost seventy-five years, from the time of the Revolution of 1789 until that moment in 1862 when the Société des Aquafortistes was organized in Paris.[1] Several reasons are cited for the supposed decline of etching; it is primarily attributed to the rise of neo-classicism as an artistic adjunct to the ideals of the French Revolution. Engraving, with its precision and firmness of line, was a much more suitable technique than was etching for rendering in graphic art the severe style of Jacques-Louis David and his followers, which dominated French painting in the late decades of the eighteenth century and the early decades of the nineteenth. David's Academy, with its emphasis on a highly polished technique, on classical order, and clear definitions, could find few commendable qualities in etching, which lends itself so readily to the personal statement, casual sketch and improvisation. As it had in several past eras, intaglio printmaking became a means for accurately, if somewhat stiffly reproducing the compositions of academic painters. Indeed, printmaking in the hands of reproductive engravers became so impersonal that mechanical devices were frequently used to incise plates, and parallel hatching was often machine-ruled. Rigid formulas for modeling were adopted. If etching was utilized at all, it was merely to "rough in" basic compositional outlines. Details, however, were carefully worked up with the burin according to a codified system of graphic description. Another important reason for the alleged decline of etching in the first half of the nineteenth century was the espousal by French Romantic painters of the new technique, lithography, invented in Bavaria in the late 1790s and exported to England and France in the first decade of the nineteenth century. The Romantic movement, which was flourishing by 1820, rebelled against the balance and logic of neo-classical subjects and compositions as well as the tight smoothness of neo-classical technique. The Romantics—primarily Delacroix, Géricault and Baron Gros—forged out a new style which was highly personal, and usually emphasized the mysterious and exotic. The cool, disciplined style of the academic painters was replaced by something new. Subject matter was chosen for its emotional power; emphasis was placed on vigorous, turbulent compositions and, especially in the case of Delacroix, vigorous brushwork and vivid color. It is no wonder that the Romantics found in lithography a medium perfectly attuned to their sensibilities. Unlike any other graphic medium, lithography encourages the artist to work with vigor directly on the printing surface and permits dynamic drawing with few constraints. Romantic artists discovered that by using crayons of varying widths and sharpness they could achieve an infinite variety of gray and black tones, and by blending the dense blacks with the transparent grays they could achieve a surface richness and range of effects which approximated in graphic terms the style of paintings such as Géricault's *Raft of the Medusa* or Delacroix' *Barque of Dante*. Between 1817 and 1823, Géricault made almost one hundred lithographs. Delacroix, too, responded sympathetically to lithography and by the time he produced his *Hamlet* lithographs in the 1820s he had worked out a process of scratching and scraping highlights into the crayon or charcoal drawing on the stone, achieving a highly effective system for creating dramatic lighting and a sense of highly charged atmosphere. Goya, working independently in Bordeaux at the same time, achieved similar effects in his bullfight lithographs of 1825. These famous prints were achieved by scratching highlights out of the broad masses of black crayon which had been vigorously drawn on the stone. Delacroix' accomplishment, coupled with the parallel work done by Goya, set a precedent for working in lithography from black to white, in the manner of mezzotint, and provided a new range of possibilities to all artists who subsequently worked in lithography.

Even more important for lithography's success and prominence in nineteenth century France are two other factors. First, in 1820 Baron Isadore Taylor organized an ambitious lithographic publishing venture, an attempt to make a pictorial record of all French historical and architectural monuments. Sold by subscription, and issued over the years a few prints at a time, Baron Taylor's *Voyages pittoresques et romantiques dans l'ancienne France* was published between 1820 and 1878. A romantic by inclination, Taylor was nostalgic for the Middle Ages and for travel to exotic places. The project was never completed even though twenty volumes containing some three thousand prints were eventually produced in an edition of 600 copies. Only one-third of the French provinces were treated before the project was abandoned in 1878. By then the cult for the picturesque, and hence demand for images of medieval abbeys, ruined castles and old winding city streets had long since disappeared. The important fact is that over the years, Baron Taylor's venture involved the commissioning of over 150 artists to make lithographs, and it thus kept lithography both on artists' minds and in the public eye.

Perhaps an even more important stimulus to lithography was its easy adaptation for use in illustrating daily and weekly journals and newspapers. A lithographic stone, unlike an etched or engraved copper plate, can yield editions of limitless size, and thus the medium was especially appropriate for use by artists like Daumier who were responsible for preparing virtually hundreds of drawings each year for the liberal journals published in Paris by Charles Philippon. Lithography, which permitted quick execution and massive editions, became the popular medium for the political cartoon. The public quickly became familiar with lithography since lithographs appeared with regularity in the daily press.

For the reasons discussed so far one might assume that etching as a creative medium had virtually withered away in the first half of the nineteenth century. It would seem that one of its functions, the mechanical rendering of images, had been assumed by reproductive engraving, while its creative function had been replaced by lithography. To be sure, most writers on nineteenth century printmaking have avowed that etching did indeed disappear and was revived only after mid-century, a revival culminating in the formation of the association of etchers (*Société des Aquafortistes*) in Paris in 1862.[2] In fact, etching never completely disappeared and if we scrutinize nineteenth century print production in France we find a surprising amount of creative etching produced well before Manet's emergence as an etcher in the 1860s.

For one thing, many etchers whom we regard as belonging to the eighteenth century lived long into the nineteenth. Baron Vivant Denon, for example, one of the great supporters of etching in the eighteenth century and himself a leading amateur etcher, lived until 1825. Also, many artists who never actually published etchings were attracted by the medium and experimented with it privately. Delacroix, for one, etched for his own satisfaction as early as 1814, and twenty-five of his plates were published posthumously by François Villot. Painters of both neo-classical and romantic tendencies tried their hand at etching, although their work was not widely distributed and is little known today. Gérôme is known to have etched four plates and Alexandre Decamps was an accomplished etcher who made prints throughout his career. Even the sculptor Barye made one etching, *The Stag and Lynx*, of 1834. Chassériau was also attracted to the medium and published a suite of fifteen etchings illustrating *Othello* in 1844. Rodolphe Bresdin was making etchings by 1835, Corot by 1845, and Eugene Bléry, Meryon's teacher, by 1836. Landscape and seascape etchings done in the mid-1830s also play a large part in the *oeuvre* of Paul Huet, a friend of Delacroix and an artist whose style is akin to that of the Barbizon School.

More than any other group, in fact, the Barbizon painters—especially Rousseau, Miller, Daubigny and Charles Jacque—embraced etching. Charles Jacque, one of the most prolific Barbizon artists, etched over 470 plates and although his work is lightly regarded today, he was a very well-known influential artist in the 1830s and 1840s. These landscape artists, whose activity centered around the village of Barbizon in the forest of Fontainebleau, anticipated impressionism by several decades. They were interested in the moods of nature; they painted intimate landscapes in which the natural forms of shadowed glens and leafy arbors are unified in an environment of air and light. There is often in Barbizon painting a sense of the growth and activity, as well as of the abundance of nature. Etching, with its sketchy, mobile lines and multiple hatchings, was eminently suited to the Barbizon style. Even in etchings where the artist's lines overlap each other in great density, the white of the paper can still glimmer through and endow the representation with vibrancy and a sense of resonating light. More than anything else, the abbreviatory or summary quality of the spontaneous etched line—more suggestive than descriptive—was in accord with the Barbizon artist's desire to evoke a sense of the unity of objects in nature.

By 1850, then, at the time Charles Meryon began to etch his views of Paris, the medium he chose, though not popular, was still practiced by artists of quality, and the Barbizon painters were at that very moment endowing it with added legitimacy. In addition to etching in France, outstanding artists such as Adolph Menzel were making etchings in Germany in the 1840s, while in England Bonington had made etchings as early as the 1820s. Furthermore, an etching club was founded in London in 1838, which Samuel Palmer joined in 1850, when he began to etch the pastoral scenes which occupied the later decades of his life. More important for developments in France is the fact that Whistler, the expatriate American, appeared in Paris in 1859 to show his first set of prints, the so-called French set, printed by Delâtre in 1858. Extremely picturesque and romantic, these etchings exhibit great freedom in the handling of the etching needle, and depend upon breadth and economy of line to suggest forms. It is said that Whistler thought of these prints to some degree as "responses" to Meryon's views of Paris. The combination of Whistler's fame and his obvious commitment to etching must have been encouraging to French artists working as etchers in semi-obscurity.

It seems clear, then, that—contrary to widely held assumptions—etching did not disappear in the first half of the nineteenth century. In fact, it continued all along to attract artists of high quality, including those, like Delacroix, whose printmaking activities were primarily in the realm of lithography. Etching certainly persisted at some level, even if it did not thrive or attract public attention. The so-called Etching Revival of the 1850s and 1860s in Paris was therefore not a true renaissance, but rather a shift in emphasis which led to the increased production of etchings and to a growing consciousness on the part of etchers of the unique qualities of their medium. Etching once again became fashionable, due primarily to the activities of several energetic individuals who publicized the merits of etchings with almost apostolic zeal. At the same time, etching received the support of influential critics. The making of etchings ceased to be the result of isolated activities and became a full-fledged movement.

A major figure in the movement was Félix Braquemond, himself a prolific etcher who had begun making prints in 1852. Braquemond enjoyed the etching process and became one of the most proficient technicians in the medium. He encouraged both Corot and Manet to spend more time in making prints, and he actually etched most of Corot's plates. Auguste Delâtre, another individual involved in the movement, was a brilliant professional printer who was interested in the etching enterprise and had printed the etched plates of Meryon, Millet, and Whistler, long before 1862. The technical expertise of Braquemond and Delâtre would probably not be especially noteworthy, nor would they have become part of history had it not been for the participation of yet another individual, Alfred Cadart, a businessman who had left the employ of the French railroads in 1859 in order to establish his own publishing house. Cadart's establishment was located on the Rue de Richelieu, not far from the Bibliothèque Nationale.

It seems that the etcher Alphonse Legros (possibly with the aid of Braquemond), actually persuaded Cadart to allow his firm to function as a center for avant-garde printmaking and as a distributor of original etchings. Cadart, then, was the entrepreneur who brought together the leading artists of the time, the best printers, and the most sympathetic critics. Cadart was an amateur etcher, and his brother, Jules, had studied etching with the artist Chifflart, who was the first etcher Cadart published after he had established himself as an *éditeur-marchand* in 1859. We may assume that Cadart appreciated the esthetic of etching. His real talent, however, lay in his abilities as an organizer and businessman. He was one of the major catalysts in the movement. Roger-Marx has referred to the "revival" of etching around 1862 as a kind of conspiracy on the part of artists such as Legros and Braquemond; they sought to infuse new life into intaglio printmaking and had the good fortune of enlisting the support of Delâtre, the master printer, and Cadart, a courageous publisher who was willing to subordinate commercial profit to the cause of distributing the prints of outstanding artists at modest prices.[3] Although Cadart must have been convinced of the importance of publishing original etchings, he must also have hoped—since he was not a man of private means—that the venture would be a commercial success.

Organized in May 1862, the *Société des Aquafortistes*[4] had as its headquarters Cadart's publishing house and salesrooms on the Rue de Richelieu. In its charter, the *Société* stated as its goal "extending and perfecting" the art of etching. Most of its members were artists; the original roster of fifty-two is extremely impressive and includes Braquemond, Corot, Courbet, Daubigny, Daumier, Delacroix, Fantin, Harpignies, Jongkind, Manet, Millet and Ribot, later to be joined by such luminaries as Whistler, Degas, Pissarro and Boudin. The main function of the association was to produce a monthly publication, a folder of five etchings by five different artists. Annual membership, which included a subscription to the monthly portfolios, was fifty francs, a rather low price considering that it included scores of original prints. The etchings were invariably steel-faced and printed by Delâtre, with twenty-five impressions on *papier de Hollande* pulled before the inscriptions were printed, to be sold in Cadart's shop as deluxe proofs at double the ordinary price. The *Société des Aquafortistes* published these monthly portfolios until 1867. At that time, they were replaced by another publication, *L'Illustration Nouvelle*, which Cadart continued to publish in monthly portfolios until 1880. In essence, the etching "revival" centered around the publishing ventures of Cadart, and included the artists listed above, along with many minor talents whose names are now all but forgotten.[5] To be sure, without the stimulus of Cadart's enterprise and the close collaboration of Delâtre's print workshop, etching might not have gained the momentum it did in the second half of the nineteenth century.

Although Cadart's activity was only moderately successful commercially, it attracted the attention and praise of the most important and influential critics in Paris, including Baudelaire and Emile Zola. Their esthetic positions offered great encouragement to the artists in Cadart's circle and was a measure of their response to the spontaneous, unstudied qualities and intimacy of etching. In an article in 1862 entitled "L'Eau-Forte est à la Mode," (*Revue Anecdotique*, April 2, 1862) Baudelaire lauded etching for its ability to express the personal character of the artist, and stated that one could "decipher an artist's soul in his rapid scribbles." Baudelaire's appreciation of the unlabored, interpretive qualities of etching must be seen against his growing feeling that photography, recently invented, might overwhelm other forms of visual art. Baudelaire consistently emphasized the slavish or mechanically quality of photography. Etching seemed to him a reaction against the inhuman influence of the camera, a reaction to the beginning of the machine age and the standardization of the picture through photography. In an etching, the personal reaction of the artist and his most immediate shorthand impression of reality is dominant.

Other writers who championed the cause of etching, notably Philippe Burty, published their essays in the *Gazette des Beaux-Arts*, a major journal founded in 1859 and still one of the leading art journals in France. Burty consistently praised etching. He even persuaded the *Gazette* to sponsor original etchers and include their work in issues of the magazine. In 1866, reviewing the Salon, Burty wrote in the *Gazette* that etching dominated the Salon to such a degree that the Salon should in fact be named the "Salon of the Etchers."

In 1863, Cadart published the monthly portfolios of the previous year in an annual album with a preface by Théophile Gautier, which summarizes the positive critical response to etching:

"In these times, when photography fascinates the vulgar by the mechanical fidelity of its reproductions, it is needful to assert an artistic tendency in favour of free fancy and picturesque mood. The necessity of reacting against the positivism of the mirror-like apparatus has made many a painter take to the etcher's needle; and the gathering of those men of talent, annoyed at seeing the walls crowded with monotonous and soul-less pictures, has given birth to the 'Société des Aquafortistes.' It has been founded to fight photography, lithography, and aquatint and all engravings whose re-crossed hatchings show a dot in the centre. In other words, they are against the regular, automatic and uninspired work which deprives an artist's idea of its very nature; and they wish their plates to speak to the public directly at their own risk and peril."[6]

It is no wonder that these critics, attracted to etching by the activity of Cadart and Delâtre, should have looked back at Meryon's etchings of the 1850s with special admiration. Although Meryon prepared his etchings carefully by studying the sites and making correct perspective drawings and renderings, his images are hardly objective city views of Paris. They are, rather, personal interpretations which invest the city with a sinister, even diabolical spirit. The buildings appear to be viewed not in full sunshine, but in cool moonlight. Although Meryon's images originated in carefully wrought drawings, they were transmuted—in the process of being etched on the plates—into bizarre and moody evocations of Meryon's secret vision of the gloomy buildings of old Paris, full of haunting associations and fraught with mystery.

Burty prepared a catalogue of Meryon's work for the *Gazette des Beaux-Arts* in 1863. In writing about Meryon, Burty emphasized the sinister character of his prints. Even earlier, in 1859, Baudelaire had mentioned Meryon in an essay, his review of the Salon of 1859.[7] Baudelaire emphasized the poetry and solemnity of Meryon's city views. He found the tumultuous sky in Meryon's prints reflective of anger and bitterness, and realized that the main point about Meryon's prints was not their realism, but their mysterious drama. Victor Hugo, as one might expect, also admired Meryon's etchings. He loved the interaction of light and shade, and the way Meryon's plates "live, sparkle and think."[8] More than anything Hugo realized that Meryon's etchings were more than pictures, they were the visions of a splendid imagination.

Meryon etched his views of Paris a decade before etching became "à la mode." The highly personal quality of his work endeared him to the critics around Baudelaire, and in 1865, three years before his death, Meryon joined the *Société des Aquafortistes* and published his *Ministère de la Marine* (DW 45) in one of Cadart's folios. By this time he was quite insane, and he could never have guessed that future generations would view him as a central figure in the history of graphic art, as a precursor of an important movement, the flowering—if not the renaissance—of etching in the 1860s.

ALAN SHESTACK

1. See especially Léon Rosenthal, *La Gravure*, Paris, 1909, p. 356; Claude Roger-Marx, *French Original Engravings from Manet to the Present Time*, London-New York-Paris, 1939, p. 7. See also Gabriel P. Weisberg, *The Etching Renaissance in France: 1850-1880*, Exhibition catalogue, Salt Lake City, 1971, p. 9 et passim. Weisberg acknowledges a certain amount of creative etching among the Barbizon painters prior to 1850. 2. For a contrary view see François Courboin, *La Gravure en France des Origines à 1900*, Paris, 1923, p. 178 and thereafter. 3. Roger-Marx, 1939, *French Original Engravings*, pp. 7-8. 4. For a thorough historical survey and analysis of the *Société des Aquafortistes*, biographies of the individuals who participated in it, and illustrations of all the etchings produced by the *Société*, see Janine Bailly-Herzberg, *L'Eau-forte de Peintre aux Dix-Neuvième Siècle: La Société des Aquafortistes 1862-1867*, 2 vols., Paris, 1972. 5. For these artists, see Bailly-Herzberg, 1972, *L'Eau-forte de Peintre.* 6. Quoted from the English translation in F. L. Leipnik, *History of French Etchings from the Sixteenth Century to the Present Day*, London, 1924, p. 106. 7. See Footnote 52 of James Burke's essay in this catalogue. 8. See Footnote 53 of James Burke's essay in this catalogue.

THE CATALOGUE

NOTES TO THE CATALOGUE

The prints and drawings follow the sequence established by *Delteil*, 1907, and all states are those of Delteil and Wright (*DW*, 1924). A state is, traditionally, any change in the copper plate, however slight.

Several technical aspects of the etchings and drawings are recorded here.

Provenance, a history of the ownership, is recorded for each object as far as can be determined. Parentheses following each owner indicate evidence provided by collector's marks documented in Lugt's catalogues, or inscribed or attributed information. Harold Wright saw hundreds of Meryon's impressions and drawings, and often marked the sheets with his opinions.

For each print exhibited all the other impressions of the particular state known in large collections are recorded. These are indicated by the name city to represent the principal print and drawing collection in each instance. Thus, Amsterdam is the Rijksprentenkabinet; London, the British Museum; Paris, the Bibliothèque Nationale, etc., with the exception of Boston PL, New York PL, and Washington LC (Boston Public Library, New York Public Library and Library of Congress, Washington, respectively).

The various types of papers are abbreviated as follows:

bl	blue paper
br	brown paper
cc	chine collé
g	greenish paper (papier verdâtre)
g/bl	greenish/blue paper
gr	gray paper
gr/br	grayish/brown paper
j	japan paper
jc	japan collé
w	white or ivory paper

In the case of a museum that has more than one impression of a particular state, the number of impressions on each color paper will be indicated; watermarks comprised of letters are also listed.

Meryon used several different papers for printing his etchings, all of them of fine quality. The most common is a fine white-to-ivory color laid paper, with the words *Hallines* or *Hudelist* in script or block letters in the watermark, often accompanied by a crest with the letters *HP* within. These watermarks appear in numerous sheets used for etchings by Bléry, Bracquemond, Daubigny, Haden, Jacque, Jongkind, Lalanne, Legros, Manet, Millet and Whistler. In most cases, either one or the other of these watermarks appears, but three cases are known in which both words appear on one sheet. These are in an impression of Meryon's *L'Ancien Louvre* (*DW* 53, V state) at the Art Institute of Chicago (09.249), on an impression of *Le Ministère de la Marine* (*DW* 45, III state) also at Chicago (09.240), and on

Bain-Froid Chevrier (*DW* 44, IV state) also at Chicago (09.238). Other watermarks carry the words *D&C BLAUW* and *J KOOL*, thicker white papers probably of Dutch manufacture. Another French white paper is watermarked in script *Contributions directes*, for example, at Chicago (27.4367), on an impression of *Le Petit Pont* (*DW* 24, III state). A paper of thicker quality, often closer to beige in color, is watermarked *J. WHATMAN | TURKEY MILL | 1853* on an impression of *La Morgue* (*DW* 36, IV state) at Chicago (27.4379), although it should be noted that this paper, without the date, was often used by Meryon in later years.

The tinted green paper (papier verdâtre) on which Meryon printed many fine impressions can now be identified by the watermark. This appears in the paper of an impression of *La Morgue* (*DW* 36, IV state) at Chicago (09.282) from the Seymour Haden Collection, in script letters *Morel|Lavenere*.

Most of the japan and china papers referred to here are not truly products of these countries, but are probably imitations of contemporary manufacture in France. In one case, Meryon printed on a paper with Japanese characters in red on the verso, a fine impression of *Le Pont-Neuf* (*DW* 33, II state) at Chicago (09.276). Finally, several extraordinary impressions of Meryon's etchings now demonstrate that he inked and wiped the surface of the plate to provide subtle tonal effects on the printed proof. While most impressions are cleanly wiped, some have thin films of ink remaining, selectively removed to emphasize areas of the image. Not only is Meryon one of the few etchers in the history of art to print his own plates well, but he was deeply involved in the technique of printing as a device which could enhance the meaning of his work. A few of these carefully toned impressions are exhibited here. For example, Cats. 64 and 69 were printed with a concern for light and atmosphere of the greatest delicacy.

The existence of wiped and toned impressions runs contrary to Meryon's own statement of 1863, in a letter to Philippe Burty, cited by Delteil and Wright, that his best prints were cleanly wiped. Meryon is quoted as saying that "those proofs, on the contrary, in which a tone of ink has been spread over the plate . . . should be rejected. When I began, I was frequently misled by bad advice, but as I have gone along I have come to insist upon this straight-forward clean wiping. . . ." These toned impressions appear only in his work before about 1855; later impressions are generally cleanly wiped, sometimes with fanatic care.

1.
Félix Bracquemond [1833-1917]
Portrait of Charles Meryon, 1853
Etching: brown ink on greenish laid paper
Plate: 106 x 87 mm. (4-3/16 x 3-7/16 in.)

PROVENANCE: B. Randall (L. 407)
BIBLIOGRAPHY: *Beraldi* 77
Lent by the Toledo Museum of Art (36.79)

TITLE PAGE: *Eaux-Fortes sur Paris*, 1852   *DW 17*
Etchings of Paris

  Eaux-Fortes sur Paris was the first suite of etchings done by Charles Meryon.
It was meant to comprise twelve large views and ten small prints of verses and
incidental items. Burty states that the twelve large prints were issued in three
installments,[1] although it remains uncertain if this was actually done. From the
rarity of the impressions of the title page, verses and incidental pieces, one might
conclude that complete published editions are extremely scarce. Indeed, it may be
that the completed suite was a reality only in the artist's imagination, a scheme by
which he hoped to distribute and sell his work. The idea for a set may have derived
from Meryon's teacher, Eugène Bléry, who produced a set of landscapes with
title page in 1850.[2] According to Burty, Meryon was inspired to make a set of Paris
views by copying Zeeman's *Pavillon de Mademoiselle* (*DW* 9). In any case, it was a
somewhat novel idea that would become more common in the years to follow.
  Burty's catalogue of Meryon's etchings appeared in two parts in the prestigious
art journal *Gazette des Beaux-Arts* for 1863. The articles were based on conversations
and exchanges of letters with Meryon, sometimes only paraphrased by Burty.
Meryon seems to have cooperated fully, but may not have been perfectly reliable
due to his unstable mental condition at that time. He was so concerned with the
correctness of details that he answered Burty's articles, using the latter's
enumeration, in the document, *Mes Observations sur l'article de la Gazette des
Beaux-Arts* (*Livraison du 1er Juin 1863*). This unpublished manuscript is at the
Toledo Museum of Art, along with a notebook full of copies of letters in Meryon's
hand and a few original letters from friends. These documents were cited in part
by Delteil and Wright, and are more extensively quoted here.
  From Burty's catalogue and Meryon's replies, one sees clearly that Victor Hugo
was the major source of inspiration for the subjects of the Paris etchings. In Hugo's
Notre-Dame de Paris there are several specific passages that Burty cites as inspirational
for Meryon's prints; Meryon responds with assenting modesty that such was the

---

1. *Burty II, 1863, p. 75.*   2. *Album de six pièces gravées sur nature près Dampierre par E. Bléry, 1850 (Beraldi 78-83).*

case. Hugo's poetry, especially *Les Voix Intérieures* (1837), is as important as his prose to Meryon. Meryon's own poetry owes a stylistic debt to Hugo, different as it is in substance and imagery.[1]

The original order in which the etchings were executed is still not clear. The numbering, and in some cases, dating of the plates in the last states represents the artist's own rearrangement of the whole set in 1861. Burty's catalogue, following Meryon's advice, adopts this order, as does the Delteil-Wright catalogue. There is some conflicting evidence that indicates a different original order, both in Meryon's correspondence with his father in the early 1850s, and in some inconsistencies in dates. For example, Meryon proudly writes to his father that *Le Petit Pont* (DW 24) is his first original print and signs and dates a proof 1850, while Burty reports that *L'Arche du Pont Notre-Dame* (DW 25) was first;[2] and Meryon's final order (1861) assigns the first number to *Le Stryge* (DW 23). In another case, *Le Pont-Neuf* (DW 33) is dated 1850 in the tenth and last state published in 1861, but was dated 1853 in states published before 1861.

The problem is, of course, Meryon himself. The closest one can approach a sense of the original order is as follows:

1850   *Le Petit Pont* (exhibited at Salon of 1850)
1851   Two dated drawings for *Saint-Etienne-du-Mont* begun
1852   Title: *Eaux-Fortes sur Paris* (only state)
       Saint-Etienne-du-Mont (exhibited at Salon of 1852)
       La Pompe Notre-Dame (first state)
       La Galerie Notre-Dame (drawing dated in December)
       La Tour de l'Horloge (second state)
       Tourelle de la Rue de la Tixéranderie (first state)
1853   *L'Arche du Pont Notre-Dame* (third state)
       Le Pont-Neuf (fifth state)
       Le Stryge (third state)
       La Pompe Notre-Dame (exhibited at Salon of 1855)
1854   *Dédicace à Reinier Nooms, dit Zéeman* (in plate, only state)
       Ancienne Porte du Palais de Justice (third state)
       Armes Symboliques de la Ville de Paris (first state)
       La Rue des Mauvais Garçons (third state)
       Le Pont-au-Change (fifth state)
       La Morgue (fourth state)
       L'Abside de Notre-Dame (fourth state)
       Fluctuat nec mergitur (only state)

---

1. For example, a similar intent can be noted between Hugo's *Les Voix Intérieures* and Meryon's work: first, between Hugo's "Oh, Paris est la cité mère!" (*A L'Arc de Triomphe*, II) and the lines of Meryon's poem *L'Hôtellerie de la Mort* (DW 37, Cat. 63).   2. In a letter to his father, dated August 5, 1850, cited in *Paris 1968*, no. 711; *Burty II, 1863*, p. 79.

The unusual quality of the individual impressions would indicate that Meryon printed them personally, at least in the early states of each etching. A fifth state impression of *Le Pont-au-Change* (DW 34) at Toledo implies that Meryon had a small press in his flat or studio, for the sheet is signed and inscribed by the printer Delâtre "printed by me at the home of my friend Meryon" with the date 1854.[1] Meryon sent his father trial proofs as early as 1850.[2] He places initials "imp" behind his own signature in many plates, indicating that he printed the impressions of that state himself; in other states, he carefully indicates whether Delâtre or others printed them.

Only in a few cases does he allow commercial printers, however competent, to print his plates in the first half of the 1850s. He printed almost no etchings in large numbers after 1855-1856, letting Delâtre[3] and others assume this task. The final printings in this suite, after some serious retouching to the plates, were done entirely by Delâtre in 1861.

"The title page," wrote Philippe Burty, "represents a block of stone with fossils and moss imprints, quarried at Montmartre, symbolizing the physical foundations of Paris."[4] Impressions were printed on brown, greenish, blue and gray papers.

2.
Only known state
Etching and drypoint: black ink on brown paper
Plate: 175 x 146 mm. (6-7/8 x 5-3/4 in.)

INSCRIPTIONS: *EAUX-FORTES | SUR | PARIS | par | C. MERYON | MDCCCLII.*
IMPRESSIONS: Boston gr/br; Boston PL gr/br; Cambridge gr/br; Chicago 1 br, 1 w; Cleveland br; London 2 br; Munich 2 br; New York br; New York PL gr/br; Paris br; Washington bl; Wesleyan University br
Lent by the Toledo Museum of Art (21.167)

---

1. *DW* 34, fifth state; Toledo Museum of Art (19.49) inscribed "tiré par moi chez mon ami Meryon/Aug. Delâtre." Burty also stated that Meryon was permitted to have a press in his studio in the 1850s; in Philippe Burty, *Maîtres et Petits Maîtres*, Paris, 1877, p. 111. 2. *Paris 1968*, no. 711. 3. Auguste Delâtre (1822-1907), born one year later than Meryon, was an important printer and publisher of etchings whose press printed impressions not only for Meryon but also Daubigny, Jacque, Bracquemond, Whistler, Millet, and Rousseau among others. He was the author of a famous handbook on etching, *Eau-forte, pointe-sèche et vernis mou*, published in Paris in 1887. For further information, see Lugt, *Marques de collections*, 1921, nos. 104-105. 4. *Burty, II,* 1863, p. 76.

Portrait of Meryon   DW 17A

This profile portrait was etched by Meryon himself, showing his image as a medallion on a block of stone. It was etched after an original drawing by Félix Bracquemond, now at the Art Institute of Chicago (38.1370).

3.
Third state
Etching: brown ink on white laid paper with plate tone
Plate: 106 x 87 mm. (4-3/16 x 3-7/16 in.)

INSCRIPTIONS: In plate along bottom: *Imp. A. Delâtre. Rue Ne St. Etienne-du-Mont No. 26.* In red ink at left: *B/a C.M.*
IMPRESSIONS: Boston; Chicago w; Cleveland w *1852*
Lent by the Toledo Museum of Art (21.142)

Dédicace à Reinier Nooms, dit Zéeman, 1854   DW 18
Dedication to Zeeman

Few impressions are known of this dedication to the seventeenth century landscapist who, like Meryon, was supposedly a sailor before turning to art. Only three other impressions are known to be printed with red ink accents (Amsterdam, Chicago and London).

Reynier called Zeeman
Painter and Etcher

Painter of seamen!
By so simple a stroke,
Your roughened hand
Knew how to describe
With ardent warmth
The allure of the sea and the billows!

Allow me to tell you
How much I admire in you
This delicate perception
That reveals the nature of a seaman!

How very easily your work
Soon brings to mind
The skillful sailor
So instinctive in his manoeuvres.

As for me, if Judgement
Did not keep me within bounds,
I would often imagine
That the paper were moist,
And that I could then detect the tar
Borne on the winds.

I long for some other age
When, sailing on your waters
I might see once again the shore,
The sea and the ships.
So that with biting mordant,
My eager etcher's needle
Might cut on the copper
All that my thoughts judge
To be great and useful
In the seafaring way of life.
You, my dear leader,
You shall hold out your hand to me.

Accept, at least, the hommage
Of this first work
Done in your simple style,
In which I have etched Paris,
The city of the galley.

My master and sailor
Reynier, whom I cherish
As my other self
May we meet in a little while!

4.
Only state
Etching: black and red ink on ivory wove paper
Plate: 176 x 68 mm. (6-13/16 x 2-11/16 in.)

INSCRIPTIONS: Along bottom: *C. Meryon fecit MDCCCLIV*

Imp. Rue neuve St Etienne-du-Mont No 26

Reinier dit Zéeman
Peintre et Eau-fortier

Peintre des matelots!
Toi dont la main calleuse,
En ta verve amoureuse,
Par de si simples traits,
Sut dire les attraits
De la mer et des flots!

Permets moi de te dire,
Combien en toi j'admire
Ce sentiment si fin
Qui révèle un marin!

Combien tout en ton oeuvre,
Nous rappelle aussitôt
Le savant matelot
Si simple en sa manoeuvre!

Pour moi si la Raison
Ne me tenait en bride,
Je croirais bien souvent
Voir le papier humide,
Et puis avec le vent,
Respirer le goudron . . .

J'espère en un autre age
Naviguant dans tes eaux
Revoir encore la plage,
La mer et les vaisseaux;
Pour d'une pointe avide,
Dans le cuivre graver
Par le mordant acide,
Tout ce qu'en mon penser
Je vois de grand, d'utile,
En l'élément marin;
Toi, mon cher chef de file
Tu me tendras la main!

De ce premier ouvrage
Où j'ai gravé Paris,
La ville à la galère,
Qu'à ton instar je fis
En ta simple manière,
Accepte au moins l'hommage!

Mon maître et matelot,
Reinier toi que j'aime
Comme un autre moi-même
A revoir, à bientôt!

IMPRESSIONS: Amsterdam w; Boston w; Chicago 2 w; Cleveland w; London 2 w;
New York w; New York PL cc; Paris w; Wesleyan University w
Lent by the Toledo Museum of Art (23.3129)

Ancienne Porte du Palais de Justice, 1854   DW 19
Old Portal of the Palais de Justice
    These two round medieval towers, Tour de César and Tour d'Argent, also
in Meryon's *La Tour de l'Horloge* (DW 28) and *Le Pont-au-Change* (DW 34), occupy
the site of the old royal palace. Here the towers and portal are enlarged out of scale,
becoming more like forbidding city gates. This is the frontispiece for the
Eaux-Fortes sur Paris. The demon holding onto the banner above is related to a
lithograph by Eugène Delacroix, *Mephistopheles Flying at Night over a City,* 1828, from
illustrations to Goethe's *Faust* (Delteil 58). The huge gate, the bursting rays of
light and the demon open the suite on a dramatic, somewhat ominous note.
    This was printed and issued by Meryon himself in the third state, from Toledo
(Cat. 5).

5.
Third state, complete with the letters, fine impression
Etching and drypoint: brown ink on white laid paper
Plate: 86 x 88 mm. (3-3/8 x 3-7/16 in.)

INSCRIPTIONS: On banner in the sky: *Eaux-Fo(r)tes | Paris | Par | (Mer)yon*; on
facade: *Paris | MDCCCL | I-IV*; in lower margin: *Paris-C. Meryon. f it MDCCCLIV
Imp. Rue Ne St. Etienne-du Mont— No. 26-*
IMPRESSIONS: Boston w; Boston PL; Cleveland w; Chicago w *Hudelist*; London w;
New York w; New York PL; Paris 2; Washington w *J Kool*; Wesleyan University
Lent by the Toledo Museum of Art (21.164)

Armes Symboliques de la Ville de Paris, 1854   DW 21
Symbolic Arms of the City of Paris
    An original invention of Meryon's, this imaginary coat of arms is surmounted by
walls and crenelated towers, with a band of three rows of fleurs-de-lis below. The
coat of arms is surrounded by olive and oak branches. The main image is a ship
with full sails on a calm sea. Burty related that the ship was copied from a
medieval stone relief that Meryon saw at Bourges; the preparatory drawing for it
is in the Bibliothèque Nationale, Paris (A.C. 8525).[1]

---

1. *Burty and Huish,* 1879, p. 54. The drawing at Paris is reproduced in *Delteil,* 1907, no. 21, formerly in the
Atherton Curtis Collection.

The first two states were only for trial, and the third state, exhibited here in a rare proof on japan paper from Wesleyan University (Cat. 6) was the published version. An unrecorded fourth state, with the name *Bella C. Landauer*, also exists.[1]

6.
Third state, completed with the letters
Etching and drypoint: black ink on japan paper
Plate: 136 x 112 mm. (5-3/8 x 4-3/8 in.)

INSCRIPTIONS: Between the branches, lower center: *C. Meryon ft- MDCCCLIV*
At bottom of plate: *Imp. Rue Ne St Etienne du Mont 26-*
IMPRESSIONS: Amsterdam w; Boston j; Boston PL w; Brooklyn br; Cambridge (Fitzwilliam) w; Cleveland w; London w; New York chine; New York PL w; Paris w; Toledo w; Washington w
Lent by the Davison Art Center, Wesleyan University, Middletown, Connecticut

Fluctuat nec mergitur, 1854   *DW* 22
(It rocks but is not sunk)
   Another imaginary coat of arms symbolic of the city of Paris, surmounted by cannons, with galley equipped with oars, and advancing under full sail. In *Mes Observations*, Meryon indicated the subject had some vague political overtones, saying that "recent major events by the Army gave special reason for this proposal, a bit daring on my part. . . ."[2]
   The drawing now at the Art Institute of Chicago (12.1572), described by Delteil and Wright as a preparatory drawing for the etching, is dated 1867, and seems to be traced from an impression of the print.[3] The etching was never published; impressions are known only at Chicago and Toledo (Cat. 7).

7.
Only state
Etching on vellum
Plate: 172 x 159 mm. (6-3/4 x 6-1/4 in.)

IMPRESSIONS: Chicago w; New York PL w
Lent by the Toledo Museum of Art (25.15)

---

1. Impressions are to be found at Cambridge, London, New York PL and New York.   2. *Mes Observations*, no. 34.   3. Reproduced in *Delteil*, 1907, no. 22.

...ell-known print *La Vigie,* "the lookout,"
...recalled his naval experiences. The
...st two states done about 1861, and in
...e for the new name. *Le Stryge* represents
...iollet-le-Duc and positioned on the
...a of the city beyond. Recently
...e enlarged tower of the destroyed
...erie rises above and out of this

...resence of the gargoyle were no doubt
...*Dame de Paris,* entitled "A Bird's-Eye
...Burty was somewhat less eloquent in
...ibed a view of

...int-Jacques-de-la-Boucherie,
..., already admirable in the
...ished. (It lacked in particular
...ched on the corners of its
...provide the ancient enigma

...wrote:

...s exist, and is in no way
...gination. I thought I saw in this figure the
personification of Luxuria [or Lust]; it is this thought which
inspired me to compose the two verses at the bottom of the print,
in which I neglected to count the syllables, ignorant as I was at that
time of the rules of versification.[3]

These verses which appear in the fourth state, define the character of the gargoyle
as a monster, "Insatiable vampire, / Eternal Luxuria, / Coveting the Great City /
As its feeding place." A lengthy discussion of the sources and meaning of the print

---

1. J. and B. Chapman, 1957, *Baron Haussman,* p. 78.   2. *Burty II,* 1863, pp. 78-79. Meryon reminded Burty
that the lines were from Victor Hugo, adding that he, Meryon, was "most honored that such pieces of [my] work
have thus given rise, through similarity of character, to such comparisons." *Mes Observations,* no. 35. The original
lines are: "Le riche clocher carré de Saint Jacques-de-la-Boucherie, avec ses angles tout émoussés de sculptures,
déjà admirable quoiqu'il ne fût pas achevé au quinzième siècle. (Il lui manquait en particulier ces quatre
monstres qui, aujourd'hui encore, perchés aux encoignures de son toit, ont l'air de quatre sphynx qui donnent à
deviner au nouveau Paris l'énigme de l'ancien. . . .)" Victor Hugo, *Notre-Dame de Paris,* 3 vols., Paris, 1836, I,
pp. 296-297.   3. *Paris 1968,* no. 710.

has been recently published by Adele Holcomb,[1] who called the Stryge itself
Meryon's "personal demon," a representation of the evil forces that play over
the city.

The dark birds, almost innocent, soaring devices to help make the space more
convincing, are also used in *La Galerie Notre-Dame* (*DW* 26) and in *Le Pont-au-Change*
(*DW* 34). They add imagery of birds of prey, associated with the half-man and
half-bird Stryge that threatens the city. "The monster is mine," writes Meryon,
"and that of the men who built this tower of St. Jacques. He means stupidity,
cruelty, lust, hippocrisy—they have all met in one beast."[2]

Le Stryge may also have been inspired by contact with photography. The
photograph *Henri Le Secq at Notre-Dame* (Fig. 2) by Charles Nègre (1820-1879) has
been dated 1850-1851,[3] just before Meryon's etching. It gives a remarkable sense
for the true altitude of the gargoyle and the scale of the city below which Meryon
captures, but it is most important as an illustration of the common interests of
Meryon and contemporary photographers in Gothic subjects and spectacular
views, here so appropriately combined. At the same time that Meryon was at work
on the *Eaux-Fortes sur Paris*, Henri Le Secq (1818-1882) was photographing at
Reims (1851) and Chartres (1852). Nègre was at Chartres in 1854, and
Edouard-Denis Baldus (1820-1882) took pictures of major Parisian sites (Place
de la Concorde, Louvre, Tour St. Jacques) in 1852-1855.[4] In the visual representation of urban and gothic subjects, Victor Hugo's most prominent followers
are Meryon and the photographers.

Although there may have been earlier drawings, the first stage of development of
the print is the study, now at Williamstown (Cat. 8), of the whole subject,
including the monster and the tower of St. Jacques. This drawing was probably
traced, or perhaps copied, onto the next drawing also at Williamstown (Cat. 9),
which is identical in configuration and size; it was then completed in modelling
adding details of the city and the birds. Both drawings were executed with a
straight-edge for sharpness, a device also used in eighteenth century views of Venice
by Canaletto. The second drawing was then copied in reverse, or possibly counter-
proofed, onto the plate, and etched to make the first state (Cat. 10). This was only a
trial, however, since two impressions were pulled. Meryon next returned to the
first drawing, and by adding all the Gothic elements at once, Stryge, balustrade
and tower, completed the plate. Most impressions in existence are of the fourth

1. A. Holcomb, "Le Stryge de Notre-Dame: Some Aspects of Meryon's Symbolism" *Art Journal* XXXI, no. 2,
(1971-1972) p. 151.   2. Quote in F. Wedmore, *Meryon and Meryon's Paris*, London, 1892, pp. 44-45.
3. Beaumont Newhall, *The History of Photography from 1839 to the present day*, revised edition, New York, 1964,
pp. 30-31, reproduced.   4. Robert Sobieszek and André Jammes, *French Primitive Photography*, Exhibition
catalogue, Philadelphia Museum of Art, 1969, no. 21-37. Henry Le Secq was a friend of Meryon who
commissioned the *Bain-Froid Chevrier* (*DW* 44) in 1864; it is not clear whether he knew the artist in the 1850s.

state, printed by Delâtre with the verses, or in later states. Meryon's working method here, as in almost all cases, is extraordinarily meticulous; it is closer to that of an engraver than to the freedom and spontaneity possible in etching, so exploited by artists like Rembrandt and Whistler. The close relationship in quality to Meryon's own impressions of the first three states indicates how sensitive Delâtre was to the artist's printing requirements; all are on greenish paper (except one impression at Cleveland on japan paper), and all are in soft brown ink, the plates carefully inked and wiped. By contrast, the impressions of the seventh and eighth states, printed by Delâtre in 1861, are in black or dark brown ink on white papers, and are much less carefully handled by the printer. The early impressions' soft tonal relationships and resultant atmosphere differ greatly from the rather stark contrasts and relative lack of detail in the late impressions.

8.
Study of *The Chimera and the Tower of St. Jacques*
Drawing preparatory to the second state of the print
Pencil
199 x 150 mm. (7-7/8 x 5-7/8 in.)

PROVENANCE: J. Niel (on Knoedler invoice); H. Destailleur (on Knoedler invoice); B. B. MacGeorge (L. 394); Knoedler, N. Y. (bought by R. S. Clark 1917)
EXHIBITIONS: *Knoedler, N. Y. 1917*, no. 109; *Williamstown 1966*, no. 250
BIBLIOGRAPHY: *Delteil*, 1907, no. 23 (repr.); *Bradley*, 1917, p. 243 (repr.); *DW*, 1924, no. 23 (repr.); E. H. Begemann et al., *Drawings from the Clark Art Institute*, New Haven 1964, no. 250 (pl. 96)
Lent by the Sterling and Francine Clark Art Institute, Williamstown, Massachusetts (1834)

9.
Study of *The City and the Birds*
Preparatory drawing for the first state of the print, before the addition of the tower and the chimera
Pencil
198 x 150 mm. (7-13/16 x 5-7/8 in.)

WATERMARK: Nude Hercules (?) on globe, with *VDL* below
PROVENANCE: J. Niel (on Knoedler invoice); H. Destailleur (on Knoedler invoice); B. B. MacGeorge (L. 394); Knoedler, N. Y. (bought by R. S. Clark 1917)
EXHIBITIONS: *Knoedler, N. Y. 1917*, no. 110; *Williamstown 1966*, no. 251

BIBLIOGRAPHY: *Delteil*, 1907, no. 23 (repr.); *Bradley*, 1917, p. 242 (repr.); *DW*, no. 23 (repr.); *Geffroy*, 1926, p. 56 (repr.); E. H. Begemann et al., *Drawings from the Clark Art Institute*, New Haven, 1964, no. 251
Lent by the Sterling and Francine Clark Art Institute, Williamstown, Massachusetts (1853)

10.

Proof of the first state before the figure of the *Stryge* (vampire) and before the Tour St. Jacques
Etching and drypoint: brown ink on greenish paper
Plate: 155 x 116 mm. (6-1/8 x 4-9/16 in.)

PROVENANCE: J. J. Heywood; B. B. MacGeorge (L. 394); A. W. Scholle (L. 2923a)
BIBLIOGRAPHY: *Delteil*, 1907, no. 23 (repr.); *DW*, 1924, no. 23 (repr.)
IMPRESSIONS: London g/bl
Lent by the Fogg Art Museum, Harvard University, Cambridge, Massachusetts. Bequest of Joseph B. Marvin (2324)

11.

Second state, completed, probably a unique impression
Etching: brown ink on greenish paper
Plate: 155 x 116 mm. (6-1/8 x 4-9/16 in.)

PROVENANCE: Mlle. Niel; A. W. Thibaudeau; J. J. Heywood; B. B. MacGeorge (L. 394); A. W. Scholle (L. 2923a)
Lent by the Fogg Art Museum, Harvard University, Cambridge, Massachusetts. Bequest of Joseph B. Marvin (2325)

12.

Fourth state with the verses
Etching and drypoint: brown ink on greenish paper with plate tone
Plate: 155 x 116 mm. (6-1/8 x 4-9/16 in.)

INSCRIPTIONS: In image: *CM*; at left side: *C. Meryon del. sculp—MDCCCLIII* (date reversed); at right: *A. Delâtre imp. rue de la bucherie 6 -* ; below: *Insatiable vampire l'eternelle Luxure | Sur la Grande Cité convoite soi pature | CM*
EXHIBITIONS: G. Weisberg, *The Etching Renaissance in France: 1850-1880*, Utah Museum of Fine Arts, 1971, no. 85 (repr.)
IMPRESSIONS: Baltimore; Boston g; Boston PL g; Bowdoin College g; Brooklyn; Cambridge g; Chicago g; Cincinnati; Cleveland 1 g, 1 j *1852*; Detroit; London g;

New York g; New York PL; Paris 3; Princeton bl; Washington 1 g, 1 br;
Wesleyan University g
Lent by the Yale University Art Gallery, Gift of "A Lover of Prints" (1928.341)

13.
Eighth state with the title, as published by A. Delâtre in 1861. The black-on-white
combination gives a crisp effect, in contrast to the soft atmospheric quality of
earlier impressions printed by the artist himself
Etching and drypoint: black on white laid paper
Plate: 156 x 116 mm. (6-1/8 x 4-9/16 in.)

WATERMARK: *Hudelist*
INSCRIPTIONS: In the plate at left: *1 CM.* In the margin: *A Delatre Imp. R. S.
Jacques—Le Stryge*
IMPRESSIONS: Chicago jc, 2 w; London w; Manchester (Whitworth) w *Hudelist*;
New York PL w
Lent by the Museum of Art, Carnegie Institute, Pittsburgh (17.30.16)

Le Petit Pont, 1850   DW 24
   Meryon wrote to his father that this was his first original etching, and sent him an
impression in a letter dated August 5, 1850.[1]
   Burty reported that:

> This view is taken from the tow-path, at the foot of the Quai de la
> Tournelle; at left, the houses of the Quai du Marche Neuf;
> Le Petit Pont (demolished and actually reconstructed) crosses the
> composition. The towers of Notre-Dame, which rise above the
> composition, are much too high, considering their real size and the
> laws of perspective.
>   We will have another occasion to note this error, if it is not
> completely intentional and in the end, perfectly acceptable. Meryon
> has no pretension that his plates have the cold exactitude of the
> photographic print. When he has taken his first sketch from a low
> point, from the water's edge for example, it is evident that he has
> placed himself at a point of view unusual for the immense majority
> of spectators; he then mounts the bank, and tacks on with
> unequalled ease, the view from the parapet which ordinarily strikes
> the eyes of the passer-by. He composes by these two operations, a
> picture which is at the same time a real view.[2]

---

1. *Paris 1968,* no. 711.   2. *Burty II,* 1863, p. 79.

Meryon responded:

> I have entered into rather long details on the subject of this piece
> several times; therefore I shall only stop at a few particular words . . .
> such as this: "tacks on with unequalled ease,". . . malicious
> reference of the author, with the purpose of reminding me that one
> of the habitual faults of my printmaking, more perceptible in this
> piece than in any other, is to execute too uniformly in all the planes;
> at the same time he takes me to task, I imagine, for having to take
> care of my own things for lack of a housekeeper. . . .[1]

Baudelaire discussed this print with the artist, and reported to Poulet-Malassis in
a letter dated January 8, 1860:

> In one of his [Meryon's] other plates, he pointed out to me that the
> shadow cast by a portion of the stonework on the side wall of the
> *Pont Neuf* [*sic*] looked exactly like the profile of a sphinx;—that this
> was entirely coincidence on his part and that only later did he take
> note of this peculiarity, recalling that this design had been made
> shortly before the Coup d'Etat. But now—the Prince is the creature
> at the present time, who, by his deeds and his countenance is most
> like a *sphinx*.[2]

The first drawing, at Toledo, is inscribed by Meryon: "taken from nature with a
'chambre claire '" (Cat. 14); it was made by tracing over an image projected
through a lens onto the thin paper. Numerous studies of specific details followed,
each carefully inscribed by Meryon with notes on textures, tonal values and scale.
In one drawing (Cat. 15), he carefully indicates all the varying stonework on the
bridge and detail in the house at extreme left; in another, dated "Wednesday
May 19" (Cat. 16), windows and rooftops are set down, along with the view under
the left arch of the bridge; small scraps of drawings—a boat, corrections of rooftops,
a window and some notes—were pasted on later. A third drawing, now at the
Bibliothèque Nationale, Paris (A.C. 8524), is a study for one arch, a tower of
Notre-Dame and detail of the laundry barge. Two additional studies for details are
in the Lessing J. Rosenwald Collection, National Gallery of Art, Washington
(B. 8690 and B. 8691), both from the Burty and MacGeorge Collections. These
drawings are preparatory for only parts of the etching, since Meryon seems to have
returned to the first, overall view, to make significant changes. The towers of
Notre-Dame are raised to show the gallery and top of the south transcept. The
arches are raised and the bridge shortened, and the angle of the opposing bank
sharpened. The first drawing (Cat. 14) was framed in pencil to show these changes.

---

1. *Mes Observations*, no. 36.   2. Crépet, 1887, *Charles Baudelaire, Oeuvres Posthumes*, p. 193.   Baudelaire
mistakenly reports that this occurs on Meryon's *Le Pont-Neuf* (DW 33).

In short, it is as if the view were changed, from horizontal to vertical format, and justifies Burty's explanation.

Meryon printed the first four states himself. All the impressions of the first state are on japan-type paper with black ink, rich and strong in effect (Cat. 17). Thirteen examples of this state are known, a large number for any of Meryon's first proofs. The third state also exists in several impressions, mostly on green paper like the print from the Yale University Art Gallery (Cat. 18). The qualitative differences between printing on japan and green papers are negligible; one could argue that it is purely a matter of taste. The fifth state, printed by Delâtre, was made when the plate was in unusually good condition as can be seen in the impression (Cat. 19) from the Philadelphia Museum of Art. Delâtre exerted extra care in the printing of sheets in 1861, and like Meryon himself, took pains to choose some fine papers as well.

14.
First study of the subject, made with a 'camera lucida'
Pencil on tracing paper
183 x 266 mm. (7-1/4 x 10-1/2 in.)

INSCRIPTIONS: In pen and ink, at top: *pris sur nature à la chambre claire- | le Petit Pont*
PROVENANCE: J. Niel; H. Destailleur; B. B. MacGeorge (L. 394 on old mat);
F. Carrington, N. Y. 1923
EXHIBITIONS: *Knoedler, N. Y. 1917,* no. 111; *Toledo 1963*
BIBLIOGRAPHY: *Burty-Huish,* 1879, p. 56; *Delteil,* 1907, no. 24 (repr.); *Bradley,* 1917, p. 229 (repr.); *DW,* 1924, no. 24(?); *Grigaut,* 1950, p. 231, no 1; *Rogers TMN,* 1963, p. 39 (repr.); *Rogers,* 1963, p. 13 (repr.); *Rutgers 1971,* pp. 7-8
Lent by the Toledo Museum of Art (23.3108)

15.
Study for details of bridge and houses
Pencil with pasted corrections and additions
159 x 307 mm. (6-1/4 x 12-1/16 in.)

INSCRIPTIONS: Various, in Meryon's hand, esp. *Petit Pont | CM f in | 1850(?)*
PROVENANCE: P. Burty (L. 2071); B. B. MacGeorge(?); Knoedler, N. Y. 1923
EXHIBITIONS: *Knoedler, N. Y. 1917,* no. 112 or 113
BIBLIOGRAPHY: *DW,* 1924, no. 24(?); *Grigaut,* 1950, p. 231, no. 2
Lent by the Toledo Museum of Art (23.3098)

16.
Sheet of studies for architectural details
Pencil on buff laid paper with pasted corrections
235 x 305 mm. (9-1/4 x 12 in.)

INSCRIPTIONS: Various, in Meryon's hand, esp. *Dessin ayant servi pr. le Petit Pont CM 1850?*; and at top: *Mercredi 29 Mai*
PROVENANCE; P. Burty (Wright inscription verso); B. B. MacGeorge (L. 394); Knoedler, N. Y. 1922
EXHIBITIONS: *Knoedler, N. Y. 1917*, no. 112 or 113
BIBLIOGRAPHY: *DW*, 1924, no. 24(?); *Grigaut*, 1950, p. 231, no. 3
Lent by the Toledo Museum of Art (22.52)

17.
First state, before all the letters and before the borderline at bottom
Etching: black ink on japan paper
Plate: 245 x 185 mm. (9-11/16 x 7-5/16 in.)

PROVENANCE: British private collection; Colnaghi, London 1973
IMPRESSIONS: Boston j; Brooklyn j; Chicago j; Cleveland j; London j; London (H. Preston) j; New York 2 j; Paris 2 j; San Francisco (R. E. Lewis 1973) j; Washington j
Lent Anonymously

18.
Third state with the initials CM at upper right
Etching and drypoint: black ink on greenish paper
Plate: 245 x 185 mm. (9-11/16 x 7-5/16 in.)

INSCRIPTIONS: Upper left: *C.M.*
PROVENANCE: P. Prouté & Co., Paris 1962
BIBLIOGRAPHY: P. Prouté & Co., *Dessins-Estampes, Catalogue "Cochin"* Paris, 1962, no. 175
IMPRESSIONS: Baltimore 2; Boston g; Boston PL g; Cambridge g; Cambridge (Fitzwilliam) w; Chicago 1 g, 1 w; Cincinnati; Cleveland 3 g; Detroit; Kansas City; London; New York g; New York PL j; Minneapolis; Ottawa g; Paris j; Princeton 1 w, 1 g; Philadelphia g; St. Louis; Toledo; Washington g
Lent by the Yale University Art Gallery, Everett V. Meeks Fund (1963.9.49)

19.
Fifth state, with the title
Etching and drypoint: black ink on chine collé
Plate: 261 x 196 mm. (10-1/4 x 7-3/4 in.)

INSCRIPTIONS: Upper right corner: *C.M.*
IMPRESSIONS: Amsterdam jc; Boston j; Boston PL w *Hallines*; Chapel Hill g;
Chicago cc; London 2; Toledo; Wesleyan University jc
Lent by the Philadelphia Museum of Art, William S. Pilling Collection
(33-72-1462)

L'Arche du Pont Notre-Dame, 1853   DW 25
An Arch of the Notre-Dame Bridge

A view of the Seine at water level; under the arch, at left, are the pilings of the
Pompe Notre-Dame (in *DW* 31), and farther along, the Pont-au-Change (in *DW*
34), behind which are the towers of the Palais de Justice (in *DW* 19). Burty informs
us that Meryon was aided by the *chambre noire* (camera obscura), but he was
obliged to completely revise the drawing in which he had been guided by this
instrument.[1] In *Mes Observations*, the artist noted that a *chambre claire* (camera
lucida) was used here, not a *chambre noire*.[2]

The first drawing (Cat. 20) now at Chicago is identical in its feeble style to the
first study for *Le Petit Pont* (Cat. 14), also made with a camera lucida. The
relationship between this first view and the completed etching is extremely close.
Only slight adjustments of perspective occur, despite Burty's claim of complete
revision. The same format of a view from water's edge, through an arch of the same
configuration, appears in the drawing dated 1852 (Cat. 44) at the Museum of Fine
Arts, Boston, where the Pompe Notre-Dame is featured. Since there are only these
two camera lucida drawings extant, one might conclude that they were done about
1850, and that the Chicago drawing (Cat. 20) set the format for the one at Boston.

The final studies for the print began with the outline for the whole composition
as seen in the drawing in the Museum of Art, Carnegie Institute, Pittsburgh
(Cat. 21). This established the basic concept as it would appear in the finished
etching. Drawings of the whole were then made, probably traced from the
Pittsburgh sheet to maintain the basic format of the arch and the pilings behind.
One such drawing, in which the background of boats, bridge and buildings is
developed more specifically, is at Toledo (Cat. 22).[3] Here the perspective of the
buildings in the distance was slightly changed, and details corrected.

These drawings were next combined, even traced, onto the final preparatory
drawing at Williamstown (Cat. 23), which is virtually identical to the etching. It is
interesting that Meryon signed it in pen and ink in the reverse; this, plus the thin
paper is further evidence that he was accustomed to using his drawings on the
verso. The reverse configuration was the design as it would appear on the plate; he
probably held the drawing to the light to copy from it.

---

1. *Burty II*, 1863, p. 79.   2. *Mes Observations*, no. 37.   3. Another drawing, at Chicago (09.297), drawn on
thin tracing paper, is a study for the three boats at left.

The etching was complete in the first state except for the finished border and some hatching lines. The only known impression of this state from the Fogg Art Museum, Harvard University, is exhibited (Cat. 24) and few are known to have been printed until the third and later states. The larger edition was printed in the fourth state, which Meryon signed in the plate with the notice that he drew, cut and printed it. A fine proof from the Yale University Art Gallery (Cat. 25) is one of two known on japan paper. The others were printed on white and greenish papers. The sixth and seventh states were printed by Delâtre in 1861, after some heavy retouchings by the artist.

20.
First study for the composition, made with a 'camera lucida'
Pencil, pen and ink on tracing paper
125 x 169 mm. (4-15/16 x 6-5/8 in.)

INSCRIPTIONS: In pen, upper left: *I*
In pencil, lower right: *A*
On backing, in Meryon's hand: *pris à la chambre claire*
PROVENANCE: H. Mansfield (L. 1342 on old mat)
EXHIBITIONS: *Chicago 1911*, no. 110a
Lent by the Art Institute of Chicago: The Stickney Collection (1909.298)

21.
Preparatory study
Pencil on creamy laid paper
165 x 216 mm. (6-1/2 x 8-1/2 in.)

INSCRIPTIONS: By CM in pencil at top: *les eiffets des Pont sont egalement bien sensibiles, puis*; left side: *les figures trop grandeur*; and in pen at upper left: *Z*
PROVENANCE: J. Niel; H. Destailleur (DW); B. B. MacGeorge (L. 394); Knoedler, N. Y. 1917
EXHIBITIONS: *Knoedler, N. Y. 1917*, no. 115
BIBLIOGRAPHY: *Delteil*, 1907, no. 25(?); *Bradley*, 1917, p. 235 (repr.); *DW*, 1924, no. 25; E. H. Begemann et al., *Drawings from the Clark Art Institute*, New Haven, 1964, p. 111, Fig. 98
Lent by the Museum of Art, Carnegie Institute, Pittsburgh (17.30.3)

22.
Study for background
Pencil on white laid paper, two sheets pasted together
186 x 248 mm. (7-5/16 x 9-3/4 in.)

WATERMARK: *Hall(ines)*
PROVENANCE: J. Niel; H. Destailleur; F. Seymour Haden (initials verso); B. B. MacGeorge (L. 394); F. Keppel & Co., N. Y. 1926
EXHIBITIONS: *Knoedler, N. Y. 1917*, no. 115(?); *Toledo 1963*
BIBLIOGRAPHY: *Delteil*, 1907, no. 25(?); *DW*, 1924, no. 25(?); *Grigaut*, 1950, p. 231, no. 4; *Rogers TMN*, 1963, p. 41; *Rogers*, 1963, p. 15 (repr.)
Lent by the Toledo Museum of Art (26.106)

23.
Final drawing for the print
Pencil on tracing paper, laid down
173 x 209 mm. (6-13/16 x 8-1/4 in.)

WATERMARK: *Vander Ley*
INSCRIPTIONS: Verso, pen and ink at lower right: *C. Meryon* and inscribed at bottom: *à Monsieur Niel de son servitur | C. Meryon*
PROVENANCE: J. Niel; H. Destailleur (in *DW*); B. B. MacGeorge (L. 394); Knoedler, N. Y. (bought by R. S. Clark 1917)
EXHIBITIONS: *Knoedler, N. Y. 1917*, no. 116; *Williamstown 1966*, no. 249
BIBLIOGRAPHY: *Bradley*, 1917, p. 237 (repr.); *DW*, 1924, no. 25; E. H. Begemann et al., *Drawings from the Clark Art Institute*, New Haven, 1964, no. 249, (pl. 101)
Lent by the Sterling and Francine Clark Art Institute, Williamstown, Massachusetts (1970)

24.
First state before the letters and minor details, unique impression
Etching: black ink on greenish paper
Plate: 153 x 195 mm. (6 x 7-3/4 in.)

PROVENANCE: B. Burty (L. 2071); L. Galichon (L. 1061); J. J. Heywood; B. B. MacGeorge (L. 394); A. W. Scholle (L. 2923a)
Lent by the Fogg Art Museum, Harvard University, Cambridge, Massachusetts. Bequest of Joseph B. Marvin (2329)

25.
Fourth state, finished with the name and address of Meryon and the date
Etching and drypoint: dark brown ink on tan (imitation) japan paper
Plate: 152 x 197 mm. (6 x 7-3/4 in.)

INSCRIPTIONS: In plate lower left: *C. Meryon del. sculp—imp. Rue Ne St. Etienne du Mont 26.*; lower right: *Paris 1853*

IMPRESSIONS: Baltimore; Boston; Boston PL w *Hallines*; Cambridge (Fitzwilliam) cc *Hallines*; Chicago g; Cincinnati; Cleveland 2 g, 1 w; Detroit; London 1 j, 1 g; London (H. Preston) g; Minneapolis; Munich cc *Hudelist*; New York 2 g; New York PL cc; Smith College; Toledo j; Williamstown g; Washington g; Washington LC

Lent by the Yale University Art Gallery, Gift of "A Lover of Prints" (1928.342)

La Galerie Notre-Dame, 1853   DW 26

A view from inside the gallery of Notre-Dame, looking out over the city, shows the Tour de l'Horloge (in *DW 28*) at center. Burty quotes from Victor Hugo's chapter "A Bird's-Eye View of Paris" in *Notre-Dame de Paris*: ". . . this dazzling spectacle of roofs, chimneys, streets, bridges, squares, spires and bell-towers toward the setting sun, on the Palais de Justice establishing at the water's edge, its group of towers."[1] Meryon obviously approved of this because he wrote in *Mes Observations*: "Here, the very appropriate quotation from *Notre-Dame de Paris* is indicated in a precise way."[2]

The black birds, which are also to be seen in *Le Stryge* (*DW 23*) and *Le Pont-au-Change* (*DW 34*) are called crows (corbeaux) by Burty. Baudelaire wrote that Meryon admired Poe, whose poem "The Raven" was first published in Paris in March 1853[3] in translation by Baudelaire just at the time when Meryon was making these three prints.

The earliest extant drawing is in the Art Institute of Chicago (Cat. 26), done with a very sharp pencil. Most lines are executed freehand, although a number of loose vertical and horizontal guide lines for perspective are executed with a straight-edge. Most attention is paid to the capitals of the colonettes, the moulding at the upper right corner, and to the two grotesque animal heads atop the engaged colonettes at upper right. These two strange heads, peering down, will be emphasized again in fine impressions of the etching; one assumes they had some powerful meaning for the artist.

The final, complete drawing is now in the Bibliothèque Nationale, Paris (A.C. 8516)[4] and was inscribed by Meryon at lower left, "Com. 17-Dec." (begun 17 December), certainly in 1852. By January 3, 1853, Meryon wrote to his father that he had begun work on this, and that he planned to enter it in the Salon in March.[5] In its close relationship to the early states of the etching (Cat. 27), this drawing is like other "final" drawings in style, and was also signed and dedicated

---

1. *Burty II,* 1863, p. 79.   2. *Mes Observations,* no. 38.   3. Y. G. Le Dantec, 1961, *Baudelaire,* p. xxiii.

4 Reproduced in *Delteil,* 1907, and *DW,* 1924, no. 26; *Paris 1968,* no. 714 (reproduced incorrectly as no. 715).

5. *Paris 1968,* no. 714.

46

to Jules Niel on the verso. Meryon must have been quite accustomed to reversing drawings for transfer onto the plate, and the frequent choice of thin, somewhat transparent papers is intentional.

The third state (Cat. 27) was the first to be issued in any number, printed and published by the artist. In this state some impressions were pulled on greenish papers, although white papers were used here and exclusively in later states. Some extraordinary impressions, like the one exhibited here from Detroit (Cat. 27), were given a fine plate tone of ink, which Meryon wiped off to enhance the bright areas of sky, reflections on the colonettes and walls, highlights on the capitals in the dark corner, and the two heads of monsters above them.

Such attention to light does not exist in very even impressions of the later states (Cat. 28), nor does the freshness of drypoint. The later states were carefully printed by Delâtre, with uniform attention to detail; the subtlety Meryon desired is missing.

26.
Preliminary drawing
Graphite pencil, partly squared in "red" pencil for transfer
248 x 164 mm. (9-3/4 x 6-7/16 in.)

INSCRIPTIONS: In brown ink at lower left: *C Meryon*
PROVENANCE: J. Niel (Wright inscription verso); B. B. MacGeorge (L. 394)
EXHIBITIONS: *Knoedler, N. Y. 1917*, no. 118
BIBLIOGRAPHY: *Bradley, 1917*, p. 253 (repr.); *DW, 1924*, no. 26
Lent by the Art Institute of Chicago: The Clarence Buckingham Collection (1938.1635)

27.
Third state, complete with the name and address of the artist, as published by the artist
Etching and drypoint: dark brown ink on ivory laid paper
Plate: 283 x 175 mm. (11-1/8 x 6-7/8 in.)

IMPRESSIONS: Baltimore; Boston 1 gr, 1 w; Boston PL 2 w; Bowdoin College g; Cambridge g; Chicago 1 cc, 1 w *1852*, 1 g; Cincinnati; Cleveland 1 g, 1 w; Detroit 2; London; London (H. Preston) g; Minneapolis; New York 2 w; New York PL; Paris; Philadelphia gr; Princeton g; St. Louis w *D&C BLAUW*; Toledo; Washington 1 w, 1 g; Washington LC; Wesleyan University g; Williamstown g
Lent by the Detroit Institute of Arts, Andrew Wineman Fund (41.42)

28.
Fifth state as published by Delâtre, 1861
Etching and drypoint: black ink on creamy laid paper
Plate: 280 x 175 mm. (11 x 6-7/8 in.)

WATERMARK: *Hudelist*
INSCRIPTIONS: Upper left corner monogram; lower left: *4*; lower center below image: *La Galerie N-D*; lower right: *A. Delâtre Imp. R. S. Jacques—265*
IMPRESSIONS: Boston PL w *Hudelist*; London w
Lent by the Yale University Art Gallery, Gift of Allen Evarts Foster, B.A. 1906
(1965.33.466)

La Rue des Mauvais Garçons, 1854   DW 27
The Street of Bad Boys

Burty describes this print as the tailpiece to the first section of the *Eaux-Fortes sur Paris*. Solid thick walls and irregular dark openings loom over the two small figures. "This piece," Burty commented, "of singular pride and power in execution, is one of those which remains a long time for its calm solemnity: it states, without ranting, this antithesis so familiar to old quarters of large centers, the sun lightening the murky stream at certain hours and gilding the walls of the sinister slum."[1] Here was the worst part of Meryon's forbidding city, about to be razed, caught in vision and in verse:

> What poor mortal was sheltered
> In this dark hovel?
> Who once concealed himself there
> In the night and in the shadows?
>
> Was it Virtue
> Miserable, and silent?
> Or Crime, would you say?
> Or some vicious soul?
>
> Indeed, I cannot say which it is.
> If you wish to know,
> Inquisitive one, go there yourself and see,
> While there is still time.

The preparatory drawing is in the Bibliothèque Nationale in Paris (A.C. 8521), inscribed with the letter *B*.[2] Another drawing, probably also of this street, inscribed *C*, is known to have been in the MacGeorge Collection.[3]

---

1. *Burty II*, 1863, p. 80.   2. Reproduced in *Deltil*, 1907, no. 27.   3. *Bradley*, 1917, p. 245, reproduced.

Most extant impressions of the print are of the third state, exhibited here in a fine impression from Burty's collection now in the Boston Public Library (Cat. 29). An equally fine sheet in the Rosenwald Collection, National Gallery of Art, also carries Burty's collector's mark. Meryon seems to have been interested in a slight sketch for this print, not as formal and exact as the rest of his etchings in the set.

29.
Third state, with the verses
Etching: dark brown ink on creamy laid paper
Plate: 127 x 95 mm. (5 x 3-7/8 in.)

WATERMARK: Crown
INSCRIPTIONS: Lower left corner: .M. Along right edge of the plate written vertically: *Meryon Imp. Rue Ne St. Etienne-du Mont 26-*

> Quel mortel habitait,
> En ce gîte si sombre?
> Qui donc là se cachait,
> Dans la nuit et dans l'ombre?
>
> Etait-ce la vertu,
> Pauvre, silencieuse?
> Le crime diras-tu
> Quelqu'âme vicieuse . . .
>
> Ah! Ma foi, je l'ignore;
> Si tu veux le savoir,
> Curieux, vas y voir
> Il en est temps encore.

Paris   Mars . . . LIV

IMPRESSIONS: Boston w *Vander Ley;* Cambridge w; Chicago 1 w, 1 w *Kool;* Cleveland 1 w, 1 w *Hudelist;* London j; Minneapolis; New York w; New York PL w; Paris j; Philadelphia w; Pittsburgh w; Princeton; Toledo; Washington w
Lent by the Print Department, Boston Public Library

La Tour de l'Horloge, 1852   *DW* 28
The Clock Tower
   The tower, restored in 1852, is shown partly covered by scaffolding. It stands at the point where the Pont-au-Change meets the Ile de la Cité. Forming one corner of the Palais de Justice (in *DW* 19), it is also the major landmark in the center distance of *La Galerie Notre-Dame* (*DW* 26). The Pont-au-Change is jammed with crowds and wagons; a heavily laden Seine barge passes beneath.
   In the sequence of development, the entire scene was first set out in the unusually

crisp drawing in the Metropolitan Museum, New York (Cat. 30). Here the whole subject is laid out, and Meryon erred in continuing the architecture of the Palais de Justice to the left of the Tour de l'Horloge, which forms the corner. He carefully inscribed the drawing for the height of a vehicle ("h-v") on the bridge, and noted details of the men on a barge, elements to be added later. One even notes framing lines to denote a proposed format. However, neither the angle of perspective on the Palais de Justice nor the exact mise-en-scène satisfied him, for another attempt was made as seen in the drawing at Toledo Museum of Art (Cat. 32). This drawing establishes the final relationship of the three round towers, the main facade and quai behind in sharpened perspective. Otherwise, the final composition retains the left half of the first drawing (Cat. 30), as one can see in the final and completed preparatory drawing (now in the Bibliothèque Nationale, Paris, A.C. 8518)[1] or in the etching (Cats. 33 and 34). The only other known preparatory drawing is for the Seine barge, without figures, also at Toledo (Cat. 31); this sheet may actually precede the composition study in New York (Cat. 30), on which the artist's inscription calls for a "boat mounted by ten men—five foreward, five aft, pulling the oars in the direction of the keel, and fending off with crossbars fore and aft." Exactly this action occurs in the final version. Although the Rosenwald drawing is without figures, it is clear that the Seine barge was planned at least simultaneously with the execution of the drawing in New York.

The final composition as seen in the etching is actually combined from two separate views. Such was also the case in *Le Petit Pont* (*DW* 24); the end result is a view that appears to be actual but cannot be pinpointed on a map or found while walking on the street. This idea is at the heart of much great landscape art, which often seeks to convince the viewer of the accuracy of the whole while actually abstracting and recombining elements from nature. Jacob van Ruisdael's seventeenth century views of Haarlem work somewhat in the same composite way, as do the compositions of Canaletto and others. Composite elements are more common than one might ordinarily think in landscape art, and what counts in the final analysis is not so much the accuracy, or the combination, but whether the final effect is convincing.

The third state (Cat. 33) presents the etched subject, lacking a final borderline. Meryon probably printed this and the next two states himself; however, the larger number of extant impressions appears in this state, most being on greenish paper. Tinted paper was not generally used in other states where the paper is white, creamy, or tan (japan). It is difficult to tell Meryon's intentions concerning the colors of papers in this case, but sufficient to comment again on his choice of unusually fine papers for printing.

The sixth state was published in large numbers for *L'Artiste* (October 1858). Delâtre printed this and the following four states. The plate was retouched by the

---

1. *Paris 1968*, no. 716, reproduced.

artist for the last three states, about 1861, altered to feature dramatic large bands of light streaming through the partly-demolished Palais de Justice. The revisions to the plate with new signboards for masonry and wrecking firms, recall the rehabilitation of the old Palais, completed in the 1850s; exhibited here is a rare proof of the eighth state (Cat. 34) from the Worcester Art Museum.

30.
Preliminary drawing
Pencil with a touch of red chalk on bridge
368 x 264 mm. (14-1/2 x 10-3/8 in.)

INSCRIPTIONS: In pen at upper left: (A). At top: *hv. hauteur de voiture/p. pierres de tailles posées en massifs pour construction./bateau monté par 10 hommes/5 devant, 5 derrière, nageant les avirons dans le sens de la quille et/armés sur les traverses de l'avant et de l'arrière*
PROVENANCE: J. J. Heywood; B. B. MacGeorge (L. 394)
EXHIBITIONS: *Knoedler, N. Y. 1917*, no. 120; *Paris 1968*, no. 717 (repr.); J. Bean, *Dessins français du Metropolitan Museum of Art, New York, de David à Picasso*, Paris, 1973-1974, no. 62, pl. 42
BIBLIOGRAPHY: *Delteil*, 1907, no. 28; *DW*, 1924, no. 28
Lent by the Metropolitan Museum of Art, Purchase, 1919, Rogers Fund (19.41)

31.
Study for a Seine barge
Pencil on gray laid paper
116 x 155 mm. (4-9/16 x 6-1/8 in.)

INSCRIPTIONS: Illegible
PROVENANCE: P. Burty (L. 2071); J. J. Heywood (Wright inscription verso); B. B. MacGeorge (L. 394 on old mat); E. Weyhe, N. Y. 1923
EXHIBITIONS: *Knoedler, N. Y. 1917*, no. 158; *Toledo 1963*
BIBLIOGRAPHY: *Rogers TMN*, 1963, p. 41 (repr.); *Rogers*, 1963, p. 15 (repr.)
Lent by the Toledo Museum of Art (23.3094)

32.
Preliminary drawing, in sharp angle of perspective
Pencil and red chalk on three sheets of gray laid paper pasted together
257 x 190 mm. (10-1/8 x 7-1/2 in.)

PROVENANCE: J. Niel; H. Destailleur (Wright inscription verso); B. B. MacGeorge; F. Carrington, N. Y. 1923
EXHIBITIONS: *Knoedler, N. Y. 1917*, no. 119; *Toledo 1963*
BIBLIOGRAPHY: *Delteil*, 1907, no. 28; *DW* 1924, no. 28; *Grigaut*, 1950, p. 232, no. 5 (repr.); *Rogers TMN*, 1963, p. 33 (repr.); *Rogers*, 1963, p. 7 (repr.); *Rutgers 1971*, p. 8
Lent by the Toledo Museum of Art (23.3100)

33.
Third state
Etching and drypoint: dark brown ink on greenish paper with plate tone
Plate: 260 x 183 mm. (10-1/4 x 7-1/4 in.)

INSCRIPTIONS: Upper right corner: *C.M.*
PROVENANCE: J. Gerbeau (L. 1166)
IMPRESSIONS: Amsterdam g; Baltimore; Boston g; Cambridge bl; Chicago 2 g; Cleveland 2 g; London 2; London (H. Preston) j; Minneapolis; New York 1 g, 1 w; Philadelphia w; St. Louis g; Washington g
Lent by the Yale University Art Gallery, Gift of "A Lover of Prints" (1928.343)

34.
Eighth state
Etching: black ink on creamy laid paper
Plate: 262 x 184 mm. (10 5/16 x 7 1/4 in.)
Lent by the Worcester Art Museum, Bequest of Mrs. Kingsmill Marrs (1926.759)

Tourelle de la Rue de la Tixéranderie, 1852   *DW* 29
Turret, Rue de la Tixéranderie

   The house stood at the corner of the rue de Coq which was demolished in 1851. One of the repoussoir figures in the foreground points to the turret. This street was mentioned by Victor Hugo in *Notre-Dame de Paris* as being among the informal and interesting areas of the city.

   The Bibliothèque Nationale, Paris, has a small study for the turret (A.C. 8522). The preparatory study is in the Museum of Art, Carnegie Institute, Pittsburgh (Cat. 35). The drawing is in pencil, with touches of red and blue which may indicate shadows. The sheet is made of several tiny scraps of paper mounted together, as though Meryon were conserving scraps of drawing paper. The final study is at Chicago (Cat. 36), as detailed as the completed etching. It is drawn on both sides of the sheet, on thin paper, and appears today mounted with the verso facing the viewer. Meryon corrected this side, erasing on the trees and strengthening some lines.

All five states described by Delteil and Wright, are differentiated by relatively minor alterations to the plate. One of the three impressions known today of the first state is that from the Detroit Institute of Arts (Cat. 37), exhibited here. The combination of black ink and japan paper gives a bright sunny effect, so different from the equally fine impression of the second state from the Museum of Art, Carnegie Institute, Pittsburgh (Cat. 38), printed on greenish paper with a warm brown-black ink. Each was printed by Meryon himself, and with the greatest care; consequently each has a unique and very delicate sense of light, determined by colors of ink and paper.

35.
Preliminary drawing
Pencil and touches of red and blue crayon on creamy laid paper, six sheets
mounted together
266 x 133 mm. (10-3/4 x 5-1/4 in.)

INSCRIPTIONS: In pen at upper right: (*A*); lower right: *d*
PROVENANCE: J. Niel; H. Destailleur; B. B. MacGeorge (L. 394); Knoedler, N. Y.
1917
EXHIBITIONS: *Knoedler, N. Y. 1917*, no. 122(?)
BIBLIOGRAPHY: *Delteil*, 1907, no. 29(?); *DW*, 1924, no. 29
Lent by the Museum of Art, Carnegie Institute, Pittsburgh (17.30.2)

36.
Final drawing for the print
Pencil on tracing paper
290 x 200 mm. (11-7/8 x 7-7/8 in.)

PROVENANCE: J. Niel; H. Destailleur; B. B. MacGeorge (L. 394); C. Buckingham
(L. 497)
EXHIBITIONS: *Knoedler, N. Y. 1917*, no. 123
BIBLIOGRAPHY: *Delteil*, 1907, no. 29(?); *DW*, 1924, no. 29
Lent by the Art Institute of Chicago: The Clarence Buckingham Collection
(38.1664)

37.
First state
Etching and drypoint: black ink on japan paper
Plate: 245 x 132 mm. (9-3/4 x 5-13/16 in.)

38.
Second state, completed, before the letters and printed by the artist
Etching and drypoint: dark brown ink on greenish laid paper
Plate: 244 x 128 mm. (9-5/8 x 5-1/16 in.)

INSCRIPTIONS: Upper right: *C.M.*
PROVENANCE: Cabanel (Wright inscription verso); B. B. MacGeorge (L. 394)
IMPRESSIONS: Amsterdam br; Boston 1 g, 2 *Hudelist*, 1 w; Boston PL 1 g, 1 *J Kool*;
Cambridge gr; Chicago 2 g, 1 w; Kansas City (Nelson-Atkins); London;
Minneapolis; New Haven g; New York w; New York PL 1 g, 1 *Hudelist*;
Ottawa w; Princeton; Toledo
Lent by the Museum of Art, Carnegie Institute, Pittsburgh (17.30.5)

Saint-Etienne-du-Mont, 1852   *DW* 30

At center is the Renaissance facade of the church; on the left is part of the
Collège de Montaigu (now destroyed); a corner of the Panthéon stands at the right.
The three structures represent diverse styles of architecture, from oldest to newest,
left to right; they also differ in function: school, church and monument. Meryon
lived only a block from this point on the rue Nouvelle Saint-Etienne-du-Mont
around 1851-1852.

Meryon executed at least three studies of the buildings in this immediate area.
One is a study for the side of the Collège de Montaigu; this is at the Toledo
Museum of Art (Cat. 39), dated February 2, 1851. Another study at Toledo (Cat.
40) depicts the same structure from the opposite side, around the corner; it is
dated one day later, February 3. This drawing also shows a corner of the Panthéon,
at left. A third study, at Chicago (09.292), related to this group, probably depicts
another elevation of the Collège de Montaigu. No other drawings are known.

The final preparatory drawing is at Toledo (Cat. 41), completed in every detail,
including the figures. This was the final stage before the preparation of the etching
plate.

Fine impressions of this etching are not always found on greenish paper, contrary
to the popular notion. The two known impressions of the first state (Fogg Art
Museum and Cleveland Museum of Art) are printed in black ink on ivory laid
paper. The only known impression of the second state (Paris) is on japan paper, as
are all the impressions of the third state (Cat. 42) in Toledo.

In the fourth state (Cat. 43) from the St. Louis Art Museum, the plate was
finished; Meryon printed most on greenish paper with very dark brown ink and
others on japan or ivory laid paper. Later stages are mostly on white or ivory
laid papers.

Meryon was quite conscious of the effects of different ink and colors of paper in the printing of his plates. His intention does not appear to favor any one of these differing materials, but to provide a variety of light effects within excellent quality of printing. The choice would seem to fall to the viewer's taste. Exhibited here for comparison are two fine impressions, one rather sharp and sunny in effect and the other clear but more atmospheric.

39.
Study for side of Collège de Montaigu at left of print
Pencil on 4 sheets added together, 2 white and 2 gray laid paper
341 x 143 mm. (13-7/16 x 5-5/8 in.)

INSCRIPTIONS: In pen at top: (B); in pencil: -2 *Fev 51*-
PROVENANCE: F. Seymour Haden (initials verso); F. Carrington, N. Y. 1923
EXHIBITIONS: *Grolier Club, N. Y. 1898*, no. 111(?); *Toledo 1963*
BIBLIOGRAPHY: *Delteil*, 1907, no. 30(?); *DW*, 1924, no. 30(?); *Rogers TMN*, 1963, p. 46 (repr.); *Rogers*, 1963, p. 20 (repr.); *Rutgers 1971*, p. 7
Lent by the Toledo Museum of Art (23.3095)

40.
Study for Collège de Montaigu
Pencil with touches of red on white laid paper
241 x 186 mm. (7-1/2 x 7-5/16 in.)

INSCRIPTIONS: At top in pen: (C); below right: -3 *Fev 51.* - | 6)
PROVENANCE: J. Niel; H. Destailleur (Wright inscription verso); B. B. MacGeorge; Knoedler, N. Y. 1923
EXHIBITIONS: *Knoedler, N. Y. 1917*, no. 125; *Toledo 1963*
BIBLIOGRAPHY: *DW*, 1924, no. 30; *Rogers, TMN*, 1963, p. 38 (repr.); *Rogers*, 1963, p. 12 (repr.)
Lent by the Toledo Museum of Art (23.3099)

41.
Final preparatory drawing
Pencil on tracing paper, laid down
290 x 166 mm. (11-7/16 x 6-1/2 in.)

PROVENANCE: J. Niel; H. Destailleur (Wright inscription verso); B. B. MacGeorge; H. Whittemore (L. 1384a); R. Zinser, N. Y. 1948
EXHIBITIONS: *Knoedler, N. Y. 1917*, no. 124; *Detroit 1950*, no. 35; *Toledo 1963*
BIBLIOGRAPHY: *Bradley*, 1917, p. 222 (repr.); *DW*, 1924, no. 30; *Grigaut*, 1950, p. 232, no. 7 (repr.); *Rogers TMN*, 1963, p. 44 (repr.); *Rogers*, 1963, p. 18 (repr.);

Peter and Linda Murray, *Dictionary of Art and Artists,* London, 1965, p. 388, no. 789 (repr.); *Rutgers 1971,* p. 7
Lent by the Toledo Museum of Art (48.6)

42.
Third state, before additional shading and drypoint completed
Etching: dark brown ink on japan paper
Plate: 252 x 130 mm. (9-15/16 x 5-1/8 in.)

PROVENANCE: A. W. Thibaudeau (L. 2412)
IMPRESSIONS: Boston j; Chicago j; Detroit j; London j
Lent by the Toledo Museum of Art (48.7)

43.
Fourth state, completed, but with the plate reduced, removing the knob on the cupola
Etching and drypoint: black ink on greenish paper
Plate: 248 x 130 mm. (9-3/4 x 5-1/8 in.)

INSCRIPTIONS: Upper right corner: *C.M.*
PROVENANCE: F. Bracquemond; A. W. Thibaudeau; F. Wedmore (L. 1053; inscribed: *Meryon gave this to Bracquemond, who sold | it to Thibaudeau, who sold it to me. | Frederick Wedmore*); T. DeWitt; Kennedy & Co., New York 1927; J. Polk, St. Louis; J. Lionberger Davis, St. Louis
IMPRESSIONS: Baltimore; Boston 1 w, 1 j; Bowdoin College w *Hudelist*; Brooklyn w; Cambridge 1 g, 1 w; Chapel Hill gr/g; Chicago 2 g; Cincinnati 3; Cleveland 2 g; Detroit; London; London (H. Preston) g; Minneapolis; New York g; New York PL g, w; Paris w; Philadelphia gr/g; Pittsburgh 1 w, 1 g; Princeton; Syracuse; Washington g
Lent by the St. Louis Art Museum (46:51)

La Pompe Notre-Dame, 1852   *DW* 31
The Notre-Dame Pump

   At this time, a large part of the city water supply was pumped from the Seine. Baron Haussmann's plans called for alternative sources which would eliminate the need for this outmoded pump. The pump, built about 1670, seems to have been already condemned at the time Meryon made the print,[1] although it was not actually demolished until 1858. The etching is a view from water level, as was the

---

1. Meryon to Paul Mantz, June 4, 1853, quoted in *DW,* 1924; and in a letter to his father, January 3, 1853, quoted in *Paris 1968,* no. 44.

case in *L'Arche du Pont Notre-Dame* (*DW 25*), *La Tour de l'Horloge* (*DW 28*), *Le Pont-Neuf* (*DW 33*), *Le Pont-au-Change* (*DW 34*) and *L'Abside de Notre-Dame* (*DW 38*). These views are all taken from a sailor's vantage point on the water. The pump also appears in *Le Pont-au-Change* (*DW 34*), behind the bridge, and in *L'Arche du Pont Notre-Dame* (*DW 25*) where its pilings are seen at left. The pumphouse was recorded in a photograph (Fig. 3) made around 1855, probably from high on the Tour de l'Horloge (in *DW 28*), showing the pump and Pont Notre-Dame, with the Hôtel de Ville and St. Gervais in the background.[1]

The pump is shown through one of the arches of the Pont Notre-Dame in a drawing in the Museum of Fine Arts, Boston (Cat. 44), which is dated by Meryon in 1852. The view was eventually realigned along the channel of the Seine in the completed *L'Arche du Pont Notre-Dame* (*DW 25*), with the pump in a minor role. In the drawing, now in the Bibliothèque Nationale in Paris (A.C. 8519),[2] the viewing position is moved back and to the right, with the towers of Notre-Dame raised slightly, becoming less compact, but concerned more with the whole pump and its site.

The etching follows the Paris drawing exactly, with the exception of the boat at right, which has been turned downstream. There are few significant changes in the states, ten in all, of this etching. The two impressions exhibited, from the St. Louis Art Museum (Cat. 45) and the Detroit Institute of Arts (Cat. 46), demonstrate Meryon's alternative printings of this plate,[3] probably dating at the time the print was first issued in 1852.

44.
Preliminary study, made under the arch of the Pont Notre-Dame (see *DW 25*, *L'Arche du Pont Notre-Dame*)
Pencil with touches of red chalk on creamy laid paper
295 x 353 mm. (11-5/8 x 14 in.)

WATERMARK: *1846*
INSCRIPTION: In pencil at upper right: *Paris | Meryon | MCCCLII*
PROVENANCE: J. J. Heywood; B. B. MacGeorge
EXHIBITIONS: Knoedler, N. Y. 1917, no. 126
BIBLIOGRAPHY: *Delteil*, 1907, no. 31(?); *Bradley*, 1917, p. 233 (repr.); *DW*, 1924, no. 31a

---

1. The photographer is unknown; courtesy of the Metropolitan Museum of Art, New York, Gift of A. Hyatt Mayor.   2. Reproduced in *Paris 1968*, no. 723. Like the drawing in Boston, this has numerous small notations in Meryon's hand to define textures and tonal values.   3. Meryon's own printings of the plate (states I-VII) are on all types of paper and with slightly varying ink colors. Delâtre's printings (states VIII - X) are on chine collé, japan collé or white *Hudelist-Hallines*-type papers.

Lent by the Museum of Fine Arts, Boston, Gift of Members of the Visiting Committee, 1917 (17.3407)

45.
Sixth state
Etching: dark brown ink on greenish paper
Plate: 165 x 248 mm. (6-1/2 x 9-3/4 in.)

INSCRIPTIONS: Lower left: *C. Meryon ft - Imp. R. Ne St. Etienne-du-Mont 26*
Lower right: *1852*
IMPRESSIONS: Brooklyn; Cleveland g; Detroit; Minneapolis; New York jc; Paris g
Lent by the St. Louis Art Museum (245:16)

46.
Sixth state
Etching and drypoint: brown ink on ivory laid paper
Plate: 172 x 252 mm. (6-3/4 x 10 in.)

WATERMARK: *Hudelist*
INSCRIPTIONS: Below image: *C. Meryon Ft. Imp R Ne St Etienne-du-Mont 26 1852*
IMPRESSIONS: Brooklyn: Cleveland g; Minneapolis; New York jc; Paris g; St. Louis g
Lent by the Detroit Institute of Arts, Gift of Christian H. Hecker (51.301)

La Petite Pompe, 1854   DW 32
The Little Pump
   This is the tailpiece to the second section of the *Eaux-Fortes sur Paris,* according to Burty. His description:

> Above, two dolphins blow water out their nostrils; below, two pipes come out of each side of the pump, climb and describe most graceful meanders, supporting overflowing cups, enlacing letters N.P.D., and ending in a swan's head. The whole is a folly of little water jets, of cascades, of unexpected leaks which form an oval frame to this rhymed caprice.[1]

---

1. *Burty II,* 1863, p. 82.

The verses read:

> It is done,
> O perfidy.
> Poor Pump,
> Without pomp,
> You must die.
> But to diminish this iniquitous sentence,
> Why not, as a touch of bacchic mischief,
> Begin to pump, impromptu,
> Fine wine,
> Instead of pure water,
> Which nobody really savors?

47.
Second state, completed
Etching and drypoint: brown ink on ivory laid paper
Plate: 108 x 80 mm. (4-1/4 x 3-1/8 in.)

INSCRIPTIONS: At bottom: *MDCCC | LIV*; below that: *Meryon - | C.M. f. Imp. R.*
Ne St. Etienne-du-Mont 26

> La Petite Pompe
>
> C'en est fait,
> O forfait!
> Pauvre Pompe,
> Sans pompe,
> Il faut mourir!
> Mais pour amoindrir,
> Cet arrêt inique,
> Par un tour bachique,
> Que ne pompes-tu,
> En impromptu,
> Au lieu d'eau claire,
> Qu'on n'aime guère,
> Du vin,
> Bien fin?

PROVENANCE: Mlle.Niel (Wright inscription verso); A. W. Thibaudeau (L. 2412);
B. B. MacGeorge (L. 394)
IMPRESSIONS: Boston w; Boston PL w; Chicago 3 w; Cleveland w; London w;
New York 2 w; New York PL w; Paris w; Toledo w; Washington w; Wesleyan
University w
Lent by the Museum of Art, Carnegie Institute, Pittsburgh (18.39.11)

Le Pont-Neuf, 1853-1854   *DW* 33

Despite its name, this is the oldest bridge in Paris, begun in 1578 but remodelled in 1843-1853. It connects the right bank with the Ile de la Cité. Here one sees the last three piers and arches of the bridge, with semicircular boutiques on the street level above.

Two early studies are known. One, in Paris (A.C. 8523), depicts one of the semicircular boutiques standing on its pier from a slightly different angle than in the etching. The other, now at Toledo (Cat. 48) sets out the basic composition, defining the major architectural lines. A completely finished drawing, known in the MacGeorge Collection seemed to be in reverse, or mounted to show its verso.[1]

The plate was then etched with bridge, river and the large house on the left. The houses, chimney and sky were systematically added; the sole impression of the second state printed on true Japanese paper (Cat. 49) lacks sky, smoke and large chimney, items which appear in the drawings. Delâtre printed the impressions of the fifth state on both ivory and greenish papers, and the sixth state, all on greenish papers. This sixth state (Cat. 50) completed by early February 1854,[2] included the verses:

> Here lies the Pont-Neuf of days gone by
> An exact likeness
> All newly refitted
> According to recent ordinance
>
> O learned physicians
> Skilled surgeons
> As with the stone bridge
> Why can you not similarly treat us?

In 1861 for the last two states, Meryon altered the plate, removing the chimneys and smoke. The houses in the background were erased and re-etched in smaller scale, giving a sense of great space. The ninth state (Cat. 51) at Yale, like most impressions of these last two states, has a more atmospheric, less linear effect.

48.
Preliminary drawing
Pencil on gray laid paper, old folds
165 x 164 mm. (6-1/2 x 6-1/2 in.)

PROVENANCE: J. Niel; H. Destailleur (Wright inscription verso); B. B. MacGeorge (L. 394 on old mat); F. Carrington, N. Y. 1923
EXHIBITIONS: *Knoedler, N. Y. 1917,* no. 129(?); *Detroit 1950,* no. 34; *Toledo 1963*
BIBLIOGRAPHY: *Delteil,* 1907, no. 33(?); *Bradley,* 1917, p. 239 (repr.); *DW,* 1924,

---

1. *Bradley,* 1917, p. 241, reproduced.   2. *Paris 1968,* no. 727.

60

no. 33; *Grigaut, 1950, p. 233, no. 9; Rogers TMN, 1963, p. 31* (repr.); *Rogers, 1963,* p. 5 (repr.)
Lent by the Toledo Museum of Art (23.3106)

49.
Second state, without the sky and chimney
Etching: black ink on japan paper, japanese characters in red ink on verso
Plate: 184 x 183 mm. (7-1/4 x 7-3/16 in.)

PROVENANCE: H. Mansfield (L.1372)
Lent by the Art Institute of Chicago: The Stickney Collection (1909.276)

50.
Sixth state with verses
Etching and drypoint: brown ink on green/blue paper
Plate: 184 x 182 mm. (7-1/4 x 7-3/16 in.)

INSCRIPTIONS: Along bottom: *C. Meryon Del & sculp. 1853 - Imp. A. Delâtre Rue de la Bacherie nº 6*

Verse to sixth state of *Le Pont-Neuf*: (in the margin)

> Ci-gît du vieux Pont-Neuf
> L'exacte ressemblance,
> Tout radoubé de neuf
> Par récente ordonnance.
>
> O savants médecins,
> Habiles chirurgiens,
> De nous pourquoi ne faire
> Comme du pont de pierre?

PROVENANCE: A. Roullier (L. 170)
IMPRESSIONS: Chicago g; New York PL g; Paris g; St. Louis
Lent by the Toledo Museum of Art (19.48)

51.
Ninth state
Etching and drypoint: brown ink on chine collé
Plate: 178 x 180 mm. (7 x 7-3/32 in.)

WATERMARK: *Hallines*
INSCRIPTIONS: In the lower margin: *Le Pont-Neuf*
IMPRESSIONS: Boston cc; Cambridge (Fitzwilliam) w; London c; New York w; New York PL j

61

Lent by the Yale University Art Gallery, Gift of Allen Evarts Foster, B.A. 1906 (1965.33.468)

Le Pont-au-Change, 1854   *DW* 34
The Exchange Bridge

Looking upstream to the Pont-au-Change at water level from a site approximately at the Pont Neuf, one sees the tower of the Pompe Notre-Dame behind the bridge, the bath houses in front, and at right on the Ile de la Cité, the Palais de Justice and the Tour de l'Horloge. In the foreground, a man in the water (Burty calls him a bather) reaches out with both arms to a boat, almost as if foundering.

Such an expansive view is somewhat unusual in the Paris subjects, seen only in *L'Abside de Notre-Dame* (*DW* 38). In 1855, Meryon followed this with two related etchings of an antiquarian nature, *Le Pont-au-Change vers 1784* (*DW* 47) and *Le Pont-Neuf et la Samaritaine de dessous la 1ᵉʳ arche du Pont-au-Change* (*DW* 46), each after a drawing by Nicolle. Both show eighteenth century views, and seem to have been commissioned by the architect Destailleur. They serve to illustrate the artist's continuing interest in the subjects of his prints and his knowledge of their history.

A preliminary study for the completed scene is known to have been the MacGeorge Collection; it outlined the whole image as completed save the man in the water.[1] Another small study is in Chicago (09.296), with the traced profile of the bridge and specific studies of the bath houses.[2] The complete and final study, one of the masterworks of Meryon's oeuvre, today belongs to the Sterling and Francine Clark Art Institute, Williamstown, Massachusetts (Cat. 52). It is complete in every detail, with clouds and balloon in the sky. The balloon bears the word SPERANZA, (Italian, "hope"), a contrast to the foundering man below. An ominous moment nearby opposes an expectant one in the distance, while on the bridge behind passes a hearse and line of mourners.

The Clark drawing sets the scene for the first five states of the print, and represents the first of several variations to occur in the sky, each altering the meaning of the print. The first state, from the Rosenwald Collection, National Gallery of Art (Cat. 54), finished except for the sky, is a proof of unusual quality, extraordinarily pure in etching and delicate in printing. The second state, also only a trial, from the Fogg Art Museum, Harvard University (Cat. 55), now completes the subject according to the Clark drawing. In this same proof, subtle drypoint both accents detail and enriches contrasts. Some minor hatching and shading appear in the fifth state, from the St. Louis Art Museum (Cat. 56); this represents the stage in the life of the plate when Meryon printed and published an edition.

---

1. Present whereabouts is unknown; *Bradley,* 1917, p. 249, reproduced.   2. This sheet is mounted backwards, that is, the drawn side is the verso. The image is squared for transfer to the plate. Other drawings are mounted similarly: The study for *Tourelle de la Rue de la Tixéranderie* (*DW* 29) at Chicago (Cat. 36) and the study for a pasture in *San Francisco* (*DW* 73, Cat. 101) also at Chicago.

In the seventh state new revisions are introduced in the sky. Only one impression is known, in the Metropolitan Museum of Art, New York (Cat. 57). Meryon has erased part of the sky, adding in pencil reclining figures of women which seem to grow from clouds, and a menacing snake and a chariot above. Like many a dreamer before and since, Meryon saw human figures in cloud forms. He drew them on two sheets, now at Williamstown; one exhibited here (Cat. 53), is a study for the figure in the clouds, that he inserted in the sky of the impression in New York. This work is difficult to date, but may occur as early at 1855-1856. It may be one of the first occurrences of the strange visions and fantastic imagery later to appear in the skies of the etchings, *Le Ministère de la Marine* (DW 45) and *Tourelle, Rue de l'Ecole de Médecine* (DW 41, Cat. 72).

These figures were never etched in the copper plate. Meryon altered the clouds and inserted a moon and vast flocks of black birds in the next major revision of the plate, the tenth state, from the Minneapolis Institute of Arts (Cat. 58). The birds take over the sky, diving low, menacing the whole city, like the predators in *Le Stryge* (DW 23) or the flocks with a holocaust that he planned but never executed in the *San Francisco* (DW 73). Baudelaire comments on this state in a letter to his publisher, Poulet-Malassis, dated January 8, 1860:

> In one of his large plates, he substituted a flock of birds of prey for a small balloon, and when I remarked to him that it was unusual to put so many eagles in a Parisian sky, he replied that this was not groundless, since *those people* [the government of the Emperor] often released eagles to study omens after the rite; and that this had been put into print in the newspapers, even *Le Moniteur*.
>
> I should say that he does not conceal in any way his regard for all superstitions, but he interprets them poorly and sees intrigue everywhere.

Baudelaire came to the obvious conclusion that Meryon might have been influenced by Edgar Allen Poe's "The Raven" which Baudelaire had translated in 1853. Continuing the above letter, Baudelaire writes:

> He [Meryon] asked me if I had read the novels of a certain Edgar Poe. I told him I know them better than anyone—and justifiably so. Then he asked me in a very insistent tone, whether I believed in the reality of this Edgar Poe. Naturally, I asked him to whom, then, he would attribute the novels. He answered me: "To a Society of literary men who were very clever, very powerful, and very knowledgeable in all matters." And here is one of his reasons: "La Rue 'Morgue.' I made a design of the Morgue. An 'Orangutang.' I have often been compared to a monkey. This monkey killed two women, a mother and her daughter. And I, too, have morally assassinated two women, a mother and her

daughter. I have always taken the story to be an allusion to my misfortunes. You would do me a favor if you could discover the date when Edgar Poe (assuming he had been helped by no one) composed this tale, to see if the date coincides with my exploits. . . ."

Don't scoff at all at this sorry fellow. I would not be prejudicial to this talented man for anything in the world.[1]

The flocks of menacing birds are removed in the eleventh state at the Philadelphia Museum of Art (Cat. 59). The sky is slightly retouched, the crescent moon remains and a number of small balloons are added. The change from the previous state is dramatic, with the sky now open and bright, and the little balloons sailing lightly into the distance.

Finally, the sky is revised in the twelfth state at Pittsburgh, printed and published by Delâtre in 1861. The moon is removed. Several new balloons appear, with evocative names. *Vasco da Gama* refers to a famous Portuguese navigator; *L'Asmodée* is the name Asmodeus, a demon in the Book of Tobias, popularly thought to raise roofs of houses and discover the secrets of the inhabitants; *le Protée is* Proteus, a sea god in Greek mythology who could change his form at will; and *le Saint-Elme* is St. Elmo's Fire, an appearance of flame on prominent points of a ship, sometimes seen in storms, taken to be a bad omen by sailors. Minor retouches strengthen the background, the pump, birds and sky in this state. As in previous states, the effect is light and breezy. Printing with brownish inks softens contrasts, in keeping with this idea. The numerous balloons add a festive mood, except for their names, some adventuresome, some threatening.

52.
Complete study for the second state of the print
Pencil on tissue paper
157 x 333 mm. (6-3/16 x 13-1/8 in.)

WATERMARK: *Vander Ley*
INSCRIPTIONS: Signed and dated in pencil at the lower right: *Meryon ft 1852* and inscribed by the artist on the balloon: *Speranza* and on the bordering sheet: *À Monsieur Niel | bien faible témoignage de reconnaissance | de son tout dévoué | C. Meryon*
PROVENANCE: J. Niel; H. Destailleur (*DW*); B. B. MacGeorge (L. 394); Knoedler, N. Y. (bought by R. S. Clark 1917)
EXHIBITIONS: *Knoedler, N. Y. 1917*, no. 132; *Williamstown 1966*, no. 253

1. Crépet, 1887, *Charles Baudelaire, Oeuvres Posthumes,* p. 193.

BIBLIOGRAPHY: *Bradley,* 1917, p. 250 (repr.); *DW,* 1924, no. 34; E. H. Begemann et al., *Drawings from the Clark Art Institute,* New Haven, 1964, no. 253 (pl. 98)
Lent by the Sterling and Francine Clark Art Institute, Williamstown, Massachusetts (1856)

53.
Anthropomorphic cloud studies (second version); recumbent figure study for the figure in the sky drawn on an impression of the seventh state of the etching (Cat. 57)
Pencil on tissue paper, laid down on white cardboard
87 x 202 mm. (3-7/8 x 7-15/16 in.)

INSCRIPTIONS: Annotated in pencil at the lower left: *Bas*
PROVENANCE: P. Burty (L. 2071); J. J. Heywood (on Knoedler invoice); B. B. MacGeorge (L. 394); Knoedler, N. Y. (bought by R. S. Clark 1917)
EXHIBITIONS: *Knoedler, N. Y. 1917,* no. 161; *Williamstown 1966,* no. 255
BIBLIOGRAPHY: E. H. Begemann, et al., *Drawings from the Clark Art Institute,* New Haven, 1964, no. 255 (pl. 102)
Lent by the Sterling and Francine Clark Art Institute, Williamstown, Massachusetts (1702)

54.
First state
Etching: brown ink on greenish paper
Plate: 159 x 335 mm. (6-1/8 x 13-3/16 in.)

PROVENANCE: L. Delteil
IMPRESSIONS: Chicago 2
Lent by the National Gallery of Art, Rosenwald Collection (B 8670)

55.
Second state before minor details completed, and fine retouchings with drypoint
Etching: black ink on greenish paper, some plate tone
Plate: 155 x 335 mm. (6-1/8 x 13-3/16 in.)

PROVENANCE: P. Burty; J. J. Heywood; B. B. MacGeorge (L. 394); A. W. Scholle (L. 2923a)
Lent by the Fogg Art Museum, Harvard University, Cambridge, Massachusetts. Bequest of Joseph B. Marvin (2337)

56.
Fifth state
Etching: gray-brown ink on white laid paper
Plate: 155 x 335 mm. (6-1/8 x 13-3/16 in.)

WATERMARK: *Kool*
INSCRIPTIONS: *C. Meryon del sculp. mdcccliiii   Imp. R. Neuve St. Etienne-du-Mont 26*
IMPRESSIONS: Baltimore; Boston; Bowdoin College; Brooklyn w; Cambridge;
Cleveland 2 w, 1 w *D&C BLAUW*; Chicago 1 w, 1 cc; Cincinnati; Detroit;
London; London (H. Preston) w; Minneapolis; New Haven w; New York 3 w;
New York PL 1 cc, 1 w; Princeton; Smith College; Toledo; Washington LC;
Williamstown
Lent by the St. Louis Art Museum (246:16)

57.
Seventh state, with pencil figures in sky, unique impression
Etching and drypoint: black ink on ivory paper
Plate: 155 x 335 mm. (6-1/8 x 13-3/16 in.)

INSCRIPTIONS: In pencil at top: *appurtient à Monsieur Burty.* Along bottom in plate:
C. Meryon del sculp. mdcccliiii   Imp. R Neuve St. Etienne-du-Mont 26
PROVENANCE: P. Burty (L. 2071)
BIBLIOGRAPHY: *Bradley, 1917, p. 251* (repr.)
Lent by the Metropolitan Museum of Art. Bequest of Susan Dwight Bliss, 1967
(67.630.9)

58.
Tenth state with birds in the sky
Etching: black ink on tissue paper with plate tone
Plate: 140 x 320 mm. (5-1/2 x 12-5/8 in.)

IMPRESSIONS: Amsterdam gr; Boston w *Hallines*; Boston PL w *Hudelist*; Cambridge
(Fitzwilliam) cc; Chicago w *Hallines*; London; Munich cc; New York PL c; Toledo
Lent by the Minneapolis Institute of Arts, Gift of Herschel V. Jones (3016)

59.
Eleventh state, with the birds removed and replaced by several small balloons
Etching and drypoint: black ink on creamy laid paper
Plate: 156 x 332 mm. (6-1/8 x 13-1/16 in.)

WATERMARK: *Hallines*
INSCRIPTIONS: Monogram in upper left corner
IMPRESSIONS: Boston w *Hudelist*; Brooklyn cc; Cambridge w *Hallines*; Chapel Hill;
New York PL cc; Paris
Lent by the Philadelphia Museum of Art: William S. Pilling Collection
(33.72.1461)

60.
Twelfth (last) state, with three new balloons in the sky as published by A. Delâtre
in 1861; here with a fine, light plate tone
Etching and drypoint: dark brown ink on gray (imitation) china paper
Plate: 138 x 319 mm. (5-7/16 x 12-9/16 in.)

INSCRIPTIONS: Upper left: monogram. In lower margin: *Le Pont-au-Change* |
A. Delatre Imp. R. S. Jacques 203
PROVENANCE: Mlle. Niel (Wright inscription verso); A. W. Thibeaudeau
(L. 2412); B. B. MacGeorge (L. 394)
IMPRESSIONS: Boston *Hallines*; Cambridge (Fitzwilliam) cc *Hallines*; Chicago
chine (?); Minneapolis; Wesleyan University w
Lent by the Museum of Art, Carnegie Institute, Pittsburgh (17.30.12)

L'Espérance, 1854   DW 35
Hope
   Verses by Meryon to accompany the etching *Le Pont-au-Change,* probably
contemporary with the first six states of that print; this proof (Cat. 61) is from the
Toledo Museum of Art:

> Weightless Air-balloon, O Divine Expectation
> Like the frail skiff which on the billows, floats
> In the careless puff of the soft south breeze;
> Come, and in the mists that the wind leads,
> Now and then make known to our eager attentions
> On the deep blue of the sky, into the placid extensions
> Where from a rich sun the copious beams
> Mark out in golden paths all glittering dreams
> Of a doubtful future: come, bring courage
> To the wandering sailor whom the storm has unsettled,
> To the brave warrior who for a better condition
> Learns to face pain from all enemy assault,
> To the poor wounded heart searching earth in vain
> For this unknown happiness he feels and longs to attain.
>
> But O sad dreamer, why thus do you sail among vapors
> When what is at stake is a matter of pictures?
> Come back, come back to earth and leave cares
> Of climbing Heaven's very steep road of ascension:
> Be afraid to tempt fate's whimsical humor
> To us always miserly of its favor.
> While Destiny has put an etcher's needle in hand
> You made a poor engraver of a weak seaman.

See in the black layer that covers your copper
Your hand leaves behind a furrow that each passing skiff
Must follow on the stormy sea
That one calls "Life," bitter, harsh Ocean
Where alas too often, false mirage,
Hope that entices us, goes to die on the shore.

61.
Second state with minor corrections of words from the previous state
Etching: brown ink on fine white laid paper
Plate: 187 x 257 mm. (7-3/8 x 10-1/8 in.)

INSCRIPTIONS: At bottom: (*Au bas de la X^m des "Eaux-fortes sur Paris"*) | *C.M.*
Mars MDCCCLIV

L'Espérance

Léger Aérostat, õ Divine Espérance,
Comme le frêle esquif que la houle balance,
Au souffle nonchalant des paisibles Autans;
Vas et dans les vapeurs que promènent les vents,
Découvre toi parfois à nos regards avides,
Sur le fond bleu du Ciel, dans les régions placides,
Où d'un riche soleil les rayons fécondants,
Craient en lignes d'or tous les rêves brillants
D'un douteux Avenir, viens rendre le courage,
Au rade matelot qu'a fatigué l'orage;
Au valeureux guerrier qui pour un sort meilleur,
De tous coups ennemis sait braver la douleur;
Au pauvre coeur blessé, qui cherche en vain sur terre,
Ce (Le?) bonheur inconnu qu'il sent et qu'il espère!

Mais ô triste rêveur, pourquoi dans les nuages,
Te promener ainsi quand il s'agit d'images?
Reviens, reviens à terre et laisse là le soin,
D'escalader du Ciel le trop rude chemin;
Crains de tenter du sort le caprice bizarre:
Toujours de ses faveurs pour nous il est avare.
Puisqu'un Destin nouveau t'a mis la pointe en main,
T'a fait pauvre graveur de trop frêle marin;

Vas que sur l'enduit noir qui recouvre ton cuivre,
Ta main laisse après toi le remous qui doit suivre,
Tout esquif passager sur l'orageuse mer,
Qu'on appelle "la Vie" ; Océan dur, amer,
Où trop souvent helas! fallacieuse mirage,
L'espoir qui nous leurrait, va mourir au rivage!

IMPRESSIONS : Boston w ; Chicago w ; Cleveland w ; New York PL ; Toledo
Lent by the Toledo Museum of Art (23.3084)

La Morgue, 1854   *DW* 36

The old morgue stood on the Ile de la Cité, on the Quai de Marché-Neuf,
between the Pont Saint-Michel and the Petit Pont ; it was later moved to the head
of the island. The building, constructed in 1568, was formerly an abattoir, a
fact that may have colored Meryon's feelings about it.

Burty's description of the scene is unusually specific and striking ; it should
remind us that his catalogue was based on close personal contact with the artist.
Consequently, Burty had a strong feeling for Meryon's imagination, as is apparent
in this excerpt from Burty's catalogue :

> In the eyes of some amateurs, this piece is perhaps the most
> remarkable of all his works. It would be impossible to extract a
> more moving treatment of a corner of houses, which, in reality,
> were far from producing a similar impression on the soul. These
> bizarre, superimposed roofs, these colliding angles, this blinding
> light which renders the contrasts of the masses of shadow so
> striking, this monument which acquires a vague resemblance to an
> antique tomb under the burin of the artist, offers to the spirit
> some unknown enigma about which the characters speak a sinister
> word ; the massed crowds hanging on the parapet of the quai look
> upon a drama which unfolds on the bank : a corpse has just been
> dragged from the Seine ; a little girl sobs ; a woman turns her back,
> distraught, choked by despair ; the policeman gives the order to
> the sailors to carry this derelict of misery or debauchery to the
> Morgue.[1]

There are prints as early as the 1830s depicting the Morgue, some with men
carrying corpses on litters. There is no precedent, however, for the intense
compacting of space and architecture, or for the audience and actors in the staffage
who perform the melodrama so carefully interpreted by Burty. Windows have
become dark menacing eyes, gaping like the vulgar and nameless mob. Below the

---

1. *Burty II*, 1863, p. 83.

bank are the public laundry barges in the river, more gloomy slum structures to enclose the scene.[1]

The preparatory drawing in the Bibliothèque Nationale, Paris (A.C. 8520) outlines the composition, without figures.[2] The only impression of the first state, in the Rosenwald Collection, National Gallery of Art (Cat. 62), a pure etching before the addition of drypoint, shows a completed scene with figures and architecture not yet fully modeled.

Two extraordinary impressions of the fourth state serve to indicate the great pains in etching and printing which Meryon took with this plate. He seems to have printed all the states up to the sixth himself, and many impressions bear evidence of this. One impression, from the Cleveland Museum of Art (Cat. 64), is on gray paper with dark brown ink. Meryon has intentionally left several layers of ink on the surface; the thicker tone is on the bank, boats and darker areas, while a lighter tone appears in all the remaining areas except around the figures, where the plate is wiped clean to show the color of the paper. The effect is to provide a delicate spot of light on the action of the figures, subtly directing our attention to the melodrama, now enacted against a dark, warm backdrop. This is less a view of an architectural monument than a little drama concerning the ambiance of Death,[3] a morality play with both audience and backdrop in the etching.

Another impression of equal quality is at Pittsburgh (Cat. 63), lightly inked and most carefully printed. It is rich in drypoint and so carefully wiped that almost no surface tone remains. The warm ink color and ivory paper increase the sense of a soft, deep environment. This is the only known case in which Meryon printed the two small plates with his accompanying verses, *L'Hôtellerie de la Mort* (*DW* 37) on the same sheet as *La Morgue*.[4] The poem adds a literary, even narrative, dimension to the etching of the Morgue, closely associating the image with the moral qualities that the artist saw in his own work.

---

1. Other views of the Morgue are known by Antoine-Louis Goblain (1779-after 1838), and Auguste-Jacques Regnier (1788-1860), in the Bibliothèque Nationale, Paris. The laundry barges (bateaux-lavoirs) also are found in numerous prints, in paintings and drawings of the late 1840s by Johan Barthold Jongkind (1819-1890) and in photographs by Hippolyte Bayard (1801-1887).   2. From the Atherton Curtis Collection, reproduced in *Delteil,* 1907, no. 36.   3. An equally fine proof in the fourth state is at Chicago (38.1630) from the Le Secq Collection, inscribed by Löys Delteil as "la plus belle épreuve que je connais de cet état." There are relatively few impressions before the fourth state. Only two exist in the second state (Cincinnati and Paris), and eight are known in the the third state, some with dedications to Meryon's personal friends (Cincinnati, Chicago, Detroit, London, New York, New York PL, Washington, and one in a private collection in New Jersey).   4. An earlier version of the poem, differing only in minor details, is inscribed in pencil by Meryon on the impression of the third state at New York PL. The theatrical qualities of this etching, and the deep mystery of the scene were first articulated by Leonard Baskin, *Five Addled Etchers,* Hanover, 1969, pp. 44-47.

Oh passers-by, come and see how like a loving mother, the city of
Paris always gives bed and board gratis to her poor children.

Without becoming pale, look upon these expressionless faces,
both smiling and horrible; they are an enigma of the future.

Here Death leads all—Love, Misery and Envy—who by their
Fate sleep in the street.

So full are the tables that even Satan trembles when the
merciless tumults roar over Paris.

Would that one might never see the heartbreaking effigy of
some beloved one on this black marble.

Oh passers-by, passers-by, pray for the deceased who are led by this
city of Pleasure in this infamous world to Death's eager grasp.

Who knows if beneath its austere aspect, Death does not
conceal from us some wistful mystery of Destiny?

Wretched humans, come, dig and delve in the earth with your feet
and hands. Each day, misery must have some black bread:
even if before evening, exhausted by piercing hunger and bereft
of all hope, your strength fails by the wayside. If you see Death
that perhaps the Lord is sending you, once again, wiping your
tears with a last effort, raise your eyes to the vaulted skies where
foreboding ceases. There, perhaps you will see that for you
the day of gentle well-being is at hand when there must bloom
in a fresh corolla that eternal flower whose seed is in the heart
of a saintly halo of Love and Happiness.

The sixth state was printed by Delâtre about 1860-1861, after retouching by
the artist. A fine impression from the Davison Art Center, Wesleyan University
(Cat. 65), printed in black ink on gray china paper, has a crisp sharp effect,
appearing more evenly lit and less clouded in mystery than either of the two
previous examples. The contrast with Meryon's fine, early proofs is even more
surprising when seeing the very deceptive Gosselin copy of *La Morgue* (Cat. 66)
which lacks mood as well as vitality of line. The force of Meryon's intentions is
lost, the subtle relationship of light and shade to mood that is the core of the
meaning of the print.

62.
First state: pure etching, before completion and darkening of the figures and smoke. Probably a unique impression, although another may exist (see *Grolier Club*, N. Y. 1898, no. 57a)
Etching: black ink on white laid paper
Plate: 230 x 207 mm. (9-1/16 x 8-1/8 in.)

PROVENANCE: J. Niel; A. W. Thibaudeau; B. B. MacGeorge (L. 394); A. W. Scholle (L. 2923a)
Lent by the National Gallery of Art, Rosenwald Collection (B 15213)

63.
Fourth state, as completed and published by the artist, and with the accompanying verses *L'Hôtellerie de la Mort* (The Hostel of Death, *DW* 37) printed on either side of the image. The verses were etched on two separate plates, and this is the only impression known with verses and image on the same sheet. An earlier version of the poem, with minor variations, is inscribed by the artist on an impression in the New York Public Library.
Etching and drypoint: brown ink on ivory wove paper
Plate: 222 x 189 mm. (8-3/4 x 7-7/16 in.)

WATERMARK: *J. Whatman / Turkey Mill*
INSCRIPTIONS: Lower margin: *C. Meryon del. sculp. mdcccliv Imp. Rue neuve St. Etienne-du-Mont No. 26 -*

Verses at left:

L'HOTELLERIE de la Mort

Venez, voyez, passants,
A ses pauvres enfants,
En mère charitable,
La ville de Paris
Donne en tout temps gratis
Et le lit et la table . . .

Regardez sans pâlir
Ces faces impassibles,
Souriantes, terribles,
Enigme d'avenir. . .

Ici la Mort convie
Tous ceux qui par Destin,

72

Couchent sur le chemin
Amour, Misère, Envie . . .

Quand sur Paris rugit
L'Emeute impitoyable,
Satan même frémit,
Tant est pleine la table!

Puissiez vous point voir,
Là sur le marbre noir,
De quelqu'âme chérie
La navrante effigie!

Passants, passants, priez,
Pour tous les trépassés
Qu' à la Mort envieuse
Amène sans tarir
La ville du Plaisir
En ce monde fameuse!

Verses at right:

Mais qui sait si la Mort,
Sous son masque sévère,
Ne nous cache du Sort
Quelque riant mystère?

Qui sait si la Douleur,
En soulevant son voile,
Du terme du Labeur
Ne nous montre d'étoile?

Allez, pauvres humains!
Creusez, fouillez la terre,
De vos pieds, de vos mains!
Il faut à la Misère,
Chaque jour du pain noir!
Par la faim aiguisés,
Si même avant le soir,
Vos forces épuisées,
Veuves de tout espoir,
Défaillent sur la voie;
Si vous voyez la Mort
Que Dieu peutêtre envoie,
Par un dernier effort,
En essuyant vos larmes,

Vers la voûte des Cieux
Où cessent les alarmes,
Levez encore les yeux
Là vous lirez peutêtre
Que pour vous va venir
Le jour de doux bien-être
Où pour ne point mourir,
Doit éclore la fleur,
A la fraîche corolle
A la sainte auréole
D'Amour, de Bonheur
Dont le germe est au coeur!

PROVENANCE: B. B. MacGeorge (L. 394)
Lent by the Museum of Art, Carnegie Institute, Pittsburgh (17.30.4)

64.
Fourth state, completed and with the name and address of Meryon and the date
Etching and drypoint: dark brown ink on thin grayish paper
Plate: 230 x 207 mm. (9-1/16 x 8-1/8 in.)

PROVENANCE: G. Petitdidier (L. 1187); L. C. Hanna, Jr. (L. 564)
IMPRESSIONS: Baltimore; Boston 1 c, 1 w *Hudelist*; Boston PL w *Hudelist*;
Cleveland w *Hallines*; Chicago 1 *Morel/Laverne*, 1 *J What*(man), 1 GDT; Cincinnati;
Cambridge 1 *Morel/Laverne*, 1 *BN*; Cambridge (Fitzwilliam); Detroit; Kansas
City; London c; London (H. Preston) w; Munich cc *Hallines*; Manchester
Morel/Laverne; Minneapolis; New York PL w; Philadelphia (Van) *Gelder*; Paris w;
Pittsburgh; Stanford; St. Louis; Syracuse University; Toledo; University of
Connecticut; Washington LC; Williamstown *Hudelist*
Lent by the Cleveland Museum of Art: Leonard C. Hanna, Jr. Collection (37.633)

65.
Sixth state, with the titles and the address of Delâtre
Etching: black ink on chine collé
Plate: 230 x 206 mm. (9-1/16 x 8-1/8 in.)

INSCRIPTIONS: In plate at center bottom: *La Morgue/1850/A Delatre Imp.*
R. St. Jacques 265; upper right: *11*; upper left: monogram
PROVENANCE: J. Michelin (L. 1490)
IMPRESSIONS: London w
Lent by the Davison Art Center, Wesleyan University, Middletown, Connecticut

66.
Edmond Gosselin
La Morgue, copy of the third state of Meryon's print without the signature or letters, ca. 1881-1882
Etching: brown ink on white paper
Plate: 229 x 203 mm. (9-1/16 x 8-1/16 in.)

BIBLIOGRAPHY: *Delteil*, 1907, no. 36 and appendix on copies; *DW*, 1924, no. 36 and appendix on copies
Lent by the Davison Art Center, Wesleyan University, Middletown, Connecticut

L'Abside de Notre-Dame de Paris, 1854   *DW* 38
The Apse of Notre-Dame of Paris
   Burty described this great panorama very well:

> The towers of the basilica, seen from below the *Pont de la Tournelle*, dominate the apse and the buttresses. At left, the three arches of the *Pont aux Choux*, above which one sees the old structures of the hospital, and immediately at left the new construction.
>
> The view of Notre-Dame, previous to all help which photography can give to draughtsmen today, is a magisterial sight. The church of Notre-Dame seems also to have exerted a great attraction on the dreamy spirit of the artist. It has dictated to a poet one of the beautiful books of our generation; it has inspired in Meryon his most beautiful plate.[1]

Meryon was obviously flattered with this allusion to Victor Hugo, and wrote in *Mes Observations*, "I am most honored by this comparison which the author makes of my work with one of the great names of our era, but only in accepting it with the humility due from my part."[2]

Meryon's interest in this subject precedes this etching by several years. A recently discovered drawing of a view of Notre-Dame with the tower of Saint-Jacques at the right at the Yale University Art Gallery (Cat. 67) can be placed stylistically between his drawings of the Pacific voyage (ending in 1846) and his early work on the *Eaux-Fortes sur Paris* (1850). It is the only drawing known of a Paris subject earlier than the *Eaux-Fortes sur Paris*. Precise rendering of the scene, characteristic of his mature works, is present, and the whole effect is more atmospheric than the more linear works of the 1850s. The dominant structures are

---

1. *Burty II, 1863*, pp. 83-84.   2. *Mes Observations*, no. 50.

Gothic, both the cathedral and tower; significantly, they are the primary elements in *Le Stryge* (*DW* 23).

The inspiration for the finished etching of 1854 may have begun with this drawing of the cathedral, later enlarged and broadened. It may equally depend on a painting of an almost identical view by Johan Barthold Jongkind (1819-1890), executed in Paris in 1848-1849.[1]

In preparation for the etching, the first study is now in the Bibliothèque Nationale, Paris (A.C. 8515), with inset framing lines to indicate the final borders. These same elements are carried over to the finished drawing, now in a private collection in New York (Fig. 4) with border lines again shown. This is a superb drawing, vibrant in line and complete in every detail except shading.[2]

The first state from the Rosenwald Collection, National Gallery of Art (Cat. 68), is incomplete in the sky, the buildings of the city and part of the cathedral itself. Shading is now added and completed in the next states. The finished fourth state, from the Cleveland Museum of Art (Cat. 69), was published by Meryon in 1854. Like several, but not all, impressions of this and the previous state, it is carefully inked and wiped. A delicate film of ink covers the entire surface of the plate, but is wiped off to accentuate the roof and transcept of the cathedral, and the embankment beside and under the bridge. Thus the direction of the light is given added emphasis, softening, with the color of ink and paper, the more linear effect of the etching. These are most emphatically opposed in the seemingly deceptive Gosselin copy (Cat. 70).

Meryon's poem to accompany this plate, *O Toi Dégustateur* (*DW* 39), was never published and exists in rare examples:

> O thou who savored each Gothic morsel,
> Look upon Paris, proud edifice that our great and pious kings
> Wished to build for the Master
> In testimony of deep repentance.
> Although very large, it is alas, still too small, some say,
> To enclose the chosen of our least sinners.

---

1. Jongkind's painting and its preparatory drawing (dated September 1848) are now in a private collection in Paris; V. Hefting, *Jongkind*, Exhibition catalogue, Rijksmuseum Twenthe, Enschede, 1971, nos. 7 and 122, and C. Gottlieb, "Observations on Johan-Barthold Jongkind as a Draughtsman," *Master Drawings* V, no. 3, (1967) pp. 296-303. Jongkind can be considered as a source or intermediary for some of Meryon's devices, notably the water-level view and the idea of monumental views of Paris in more or less realistic format and style; see V. Hefting, ibid, nos. 7, 8, 12 and 14. 2. The Paris drawing is reproduced by *Delteil*, 1907, no. 38; *Bradley*, 1917, p. 225, and in *Paris 1968*, no. 734. In addition, nine studies of individual details are in the Bibliothèque Nationale, Paris (A.C. 8527). The finished drawing, in pencil, came from the MacGeorge Collection, and is reproduced by *Bradley*, 1917, p. 227.

67.
View of Notre-Dame with the north side of the Ile de la Cité, ca. 1848-1849
Graphite pencil on cream paper washed with gum arabic
212 x 388 mm. (8-3/8 x 15-1/4 in.)

INSCRIPTIONS: Inscribed in pencil at lower right: *Paris*
PROVENANCE: J. Niel; H. Destailleur (both inscribed verso); Claude Aubry,
Paris; Shepherd Gallery, N. Y. 1973
Lent by the Yale University Art Gallery, Everett V. Meeks, B.A. 1901, Fund
(1973.59)

68.
First state, unique
Etching: black ink on white laid paper
Plate: 165 x 300 mm. (6-1/2 x 11-13/16 in.)

WATERMARK: *Cribot*(?)
PROVENANCE: J. Niel; J. J. Heywood; B. B. MacGeorge (L. 394); A. Curtis;
A. W. Scholle (L. 2923a)
Lent by the National Gallery of Art, Rosenwald Collection (B 21968)

69.
Fourth state
Etching and drypoint: dark brown ink on fine ivory laid paper
Plate: 166 x 300 mm. (6-1/2 x 11-13/16 in.)

WATERMARK: *DT*
INSCRIPTIONS: From left across bottom in margin: *C. Meryon - del. sculp. mdcccliv*
Imp. Rue Neuve St. Etienne-du-Mont 26
IMPRESSIONS: Baltimore; Boston w; Boston PL w; Cleveland *J. Whatman*;
Cincinnati; Chicago; Cambridge w; Detroit; London; Minneapolis 3; New
Haven w; New York w; New York PL; Paris w; Princeton; Philadelphia;
Williamstown
Lent by the Cleveland Museum of Art, John L. Severance Collection (42.751)

70.
Edmond Gosselin
L'Abside de Notre-Dame, copy of the third state of Meryon's print
Etching: brown ink on white paper
Plate: 166 x 293 mm. (6-1/2 x 11-9/16 in.)

INSCRIPTIONS: In plate at lower right: *1882*
Lent by the Davison Art Center, Wesleyan University, Middletown, Connecticut

Le Tombeau de Molière, 1854   *DW* 40
Molière's Tomb

This is the end-piece to the *Eaux-Fortes sur Paris.* It represents the tomb of Molière at Père-Lachaise Cemetery. Above the tomb is a flaming cup, behind it shine the rays of what Burty called "a mysterious star." Below is the symbolic ship of Paris seen in the *Armes Symboliques de la Ville de Paris (DW* 21); laurel wreaths surround the image.

Meyron reports that he gave the plate to the printer Delâtre, "and wished it destroyed,"[1] although the plate is today in the printroom of the Metropolitan Museum of Art, New York. Two preparatory drawings, exhibited at the Grolier Club in New York, 1898, are now in the Lessing J. Rosenwald Collection, National Gallery of Art, Washington (B. 8695 and B. 8704); still another was in the MacGeorge Collection.[2] An impression of the second state (Cat. 71) is exhibited from Toledo.

71.
Second state, a fine impression with full plate tone
Etching and drypoint: dark brown ink on ivory laid paper
Plate: 67 x 69 mm. (2-5/8 x 2-3/4 in.)

INSCRIPTIONS: Lower left: *C. Meryon / ft MDCCCLIV*; lower right: *Imp. R. Ne St. Etienne / du Mont - No 26*
PROVENANCE: P. Burty (L. 2071)
IMPRESSIONS: Boston w; Cambridge w; Cleveland w; Chicago 1 g, 1 *D&C Blauw*, 1 w, 1 *C&W/Comp*; London w; New York PL 2; New York 2 w; Washington 2, 1 *Hudelist*; Wesleyan University w
Lent by the Toledo Museum of Art (21.165)

Tourelle, Rue de l'Ecole-de-Médecine, 1861   *DW* 41
Turret, Rue de l'Ecole-de-Médecine

This small tower formed the corner of the house in which Charlotte Corday assassinated Jean-Paul Marat. Two roofers on the chimney nearby see a vision of figures in the sky, of which the crowd below is oblivious.

---

1. *Mes Observations,* no. 51.   2. Both are from the collection of F. Seymour Haden. The third drawing was exhibited at *Knoedler N.Y. 1917,* no. 135.

The verse beneath the image reads, "Holy, inviolable truth, Divine torch of the soul; / When chaos is on earth, / You descend from the skies to enlighten man / And to regulate the decrees of strict justice."

By 1863, when he wrote his reply to Burty's catalogue, Meryon thought this etching to be his best work. The greater clarity, simple order and direct meanings of the *Eaux-Fortes sur Paris* did not interest him as much as the veiled allusions and visionary figures. He wrote:

> This piece, although small, is in my opinion (and I have strong reasons to think so), my masterpiece: I speak of the state of this print in which is the composition of the sky: that is, on one side Justice who, in sight of Truth, shimmering in light, swoons, her balance and sword slip out of her hands; on the other, above, below the figure of a young child, seen from behind, the hair disheveled, the hands pressed to the forehead as though beneath the blow of an acute pain; stopped suddenly in her flight, rising, the two small wings fall away, detached, this very singular allusion, precise and direct, which comprises almost in itself all the interest of the subject, which I shall call finally Innocence wronged, violated. . . . I have already explained once, in a rather complete manner, the significance that I wished to give to this composition, in a letter written to M. Ph. Burty; I shall not return to that here, while those who will examine it with interest and attention should understand, find the true and whole meaning, a meaning to which I attach, I repeat, the greatest importance.

> This first wish indicated, passing to minor matters, I shall give a short explanation relative to the idea, aided a bit by chance which made me retain the word *CABAT*, that one sees written on one section of the turret. It is the word *TABAC* (tobacco) that one must read, the sign of a merchant on the street, of which the symbol stands out in print. The letters of this word, transposed as by an error of the etcher, give therefore *CABAT*. Now, I made use of this word-play, to express first the precedence that I give to a number of sustenances of the greatest usefulness (bread first of all), above this plant, which they abuse, without a doubt, in our civilized cities, and which should only be used to purify the blood and of which the effect is the contrary, from the immoderate use which we make of it, to exhaust the finances of a great number of individuals.

In the second plane in another sense, in this word *CABAT* one can
see the intervention of a fatality playing its role here, which I
evoke on good authority, as much as it is possible to do so.[1]

The full sketch for the composition, reworked, is at Paris (A.C. 8526);[2] a small
study for the spire atop the house is at Toledo (23.3217). As is the case with many
of the prints of the 1860s, Meryon labored over the plate at great length, as
indicated by numerous states with but miniscule differences. The fine impression
of a hitherto undescribed state (Cat. 72) from the Cleveland Museum of Art is
dated 1861, the year of its origin. The plate was first printed extensively in the last
two (twelfth and thirteenth) states for the *Gazette des Beaux-Arts* in 1863.

72.
Undescribed state, between *DW* ninth and tenth states, a unique impression
Etching and drypoint: brown-black ink on china paper
Plate: 214 x 132 mm. (8-3/8 x 5-1/8 in.)

INSCRIPTIONS: Monogram at top of image; in margin of plate: *TOURELLE | RUE
DE L'ECOLE DE MÉDECINE, 22 | PARIS | Imp. Pierron r Montfaucon 1, Paris*
In bottom margin of sheet, in arist's hand: *À Monsieur Philippe Burty. | Sainte,
Indissoluble Verité; Divin Flambeau | de l'âme; quand le Chaos est sur la Terre, tu | descends
des Cieux pour éclaireir les Hommes et | régler les décréts de la stricte Justice . . . |*
C.M. 7 Juillet 1861 26 Juin
PROVENANCE: P. Burty (L. 2071); J. Day (L. 526)
Lent by the Cleveland Museum of Art, Milton Curtiss Rose Collection in
Memory of Evelyn Curtiss Rose (68.253)

Le Rue des Chantres, 1862   *DW* 42

This narrow street, filled with passers-by, police and sailors, with the high dark
walls of houses on either side, leads to a bright house in the middle distance,
above which rises the spire which Viollet-le-Duc added to Notre-Dame.

A separate study for the spire from the Toledo Museum of Art (Cat. 73) is dated
three times: June 27th, June 28th, and July 2nd. The larger drawing for the
composition, also from Toledo (Cat. 74) outlines the right wall of the street, the
house at the end and the spire above, and should be later than the spire study.
The left wall of the street appears to have been added later still. In this way
Meryon's etching was composed from two drawings differing very slightly in
vantage point,[3] providing, in the end, a likeness for the narrow street in the old city.

All impressions of the etching are on white or gray papers; Meryon seems to

---

1. *Mes Observations*, no. 53.   2. *Delteil*, 1907, no. 41, reproduced.   3. For a discussion of Meryon's composite
views, see Philip Cate, "Meryon's Paris," *Print Collector's Newsletter* II, no. 4, (September-October 1971)
pp. 77-79.

have printed the first four states in small numbers. The fifth state (Cat. 75) from the Yale University Art Gallery, was printed by Delâtre in one hundred impressions, with almost no significant diversions from Meryon's own printing.

73.
Study for the spire
Pencil with touches of red on gray wove paper
147 x 53 mm. (5-13/16 x 2-1/16 in.)

INSCRIPTIONS: In pencil at upper right: *27 Jn/28 id.*, at lower right: *2 Juil*
in pen lower right: *C.M/1862*
PROVENANCE: B. B. MacGeorge (L. 394, on old mat); E. Weyhe, N. Y. 1923
EXHIBITIONS: *Knoedler, N. Y. 1917*, no. 137; *Toledo 1963*
BIBLIOGRAPHY: *DW*, 1924, no. 42; *Rogers TMN*, 1963, p. 35; *Rogers*, 1963, p. 9
(repr.); *Rutgers 1971*, p. 9
Lent by the Toledo Museum of Art (23.3093)

74.
Study for the print
Pencil and touches of red on gray wove paper
279 x 83 mm. (11 x 3-1/4 in.)

INSCRIPTIONS: In pen on right side: *Rue des Chantres*; in pencil below: *4 arches
visible sur lofte 2 a gauche confine*; in pen lower left: *CM fe. 1862*
PROVENANCE: B. B. MacGeorge (L. 394, on old mat); F. Carrington, N. Y. 1923
EXHIBITIONS: *Knoedler, N. Y. 1917*, no. 136; *Toledo 1963*
BIBLIOGRAPHY: *DW*, 1924, no. 42; *Grigaut*, 1950, p. 233, no. 12; *Rogers TMN*,
1963, p. 35 (repr); *Rogers*, 1963, p. 9 (repr.); *Rutgers 1971*, p. 9
Lent by the Toledo Museum of Art (23.3115)

75.
Fifth state
Etching and drypoint: dark brown ink in creamy laid paper
Plate: 300 x 147 mm. (11-13/16 x 5-13/16 in.)

WATERMARK: Coat of Arms (?)
INSCRIPTIONS: Monogram at top with letters *J.B.*; along bottom in margin:
Chez ROCHOUX Quai de l' Horloge, 19; center: *Rue des Chantres*; below that: *Paris,
MDCCLXII*; at right: *Pierron Imp. r. Montfaucon 1*

IMPRESSIONS: Boston w; Bowdoin College; Cambridge w; Cambridge (Fitzwilliam)
w; Chicago w *WJ . . . D*; Cleveland; London w; Minneapolis; New York PL
Lent by the Yale University Art Gallery, Gift of Allen Evarts Foster, B.A. 1906
(1965.33.469)

Collège Henri IV, 1864   DW 43

A bird's-eye view of the famous secondary school also known as the Lycée
Napoléon, taken from the summit of the Panthéon. Commissioned by Philippon
and Salicis, two old friends who were educated there, this etching is one of
Meryon's largest works.

A presumed early sketch set out the whole scheme which was divided into six
sections for further development. Meryon seems to have started with the upper
left corner, beginning with a drawing now in the Museum of Fine Arts, Boston
(58.335), which he inscribed "premier dessin fait sur place" ("first drawing made
on the site"). Its sharp perspective did not satisfy him, and it was altered in
another version of the same section in the Rosenwald Collection, National Gallery
of Art (Cat. 76). He then drew the next section, also in the Rosenwald Collection
(Cat. 77), which forms the upper center of the final composition. The distant
view beyond the houses immediately beyond the Collège was not added at this time
in either drawing, and the two portrait medallions in the center were never used.

The fore- and backgrounds in the drawings of the Collège Meryon added from
his imagination. The fourth state (Cat. 78) from the Bowdoin College Museum of
Art has a mountainous landscape at upper left and a fanciful ocean with sea gods
behind, reminiscences of the travels of the artist and his two patrons. Peopled
with strange figures, the foreground is completely out of perspective with the rest.
Meryon described almost every aspect of this print in labored detail; accordingly,
the foreground showed

> a suite of sliding or skating people. Permit me to say that now that
> I have had enough experience of life I consider this practice very
> important for young people . . . the three little figures further to
> the left talk or discuss. . . . In the light of the importance of the
> thought which I have attached to it, the figure that represents
> Generosity is much larger than the others. I have taken, moreover,
> this license to imagine ice following a part of the facade of the
> foreground, although nearby the trees are adorned with their
> leaves.[1]

---

1. This long letter describing the print was written by Meryon in 1864 and appeared in *L'Union des Arts* in that
year; it is quoted here from *Burty and Huish*, 1879, pp. 91-92. Numerous details of the background of mountains
and ocean are also described.

In the seventh through the eleventh states, Meryon replaced the fantastic mountains and ocean behind the Collège with a more realistic panorama of houses and streets. The tenth state (Cat. 79), from Wesleyan University, was also carefully described by Meryon:

> In this piece, an exact and minute reproduction of reality, I have placed in the middle of the upper part two medallions bearing the images of the two sovereigns under whose invocation the Lycée was established [equestrian statues of Henri IV and Napoléon III]. Between these medallions, a tablet on which one reads the Latin device by which I have proposed to resume the thought which has presided over my work.
>
> In this state, the bottom is in all aspects cut with precision bordering on minutiae. I cite, towards the center of the Collège, on the facade of the main part of the building, sharing a view on one of the courtyards, a stone sundial standing on the roof; in the left corner a part of Saint-Etienne-du-Mont and of the Ecole Polytechnique; in the upper right-hand corner, Saint-Médard; at the farthest limit of the left-hand corner, the entrance, on the quai, of the wine warehouse; beneath the right medallion, the prison of Sainte-Pélagie, where we can distinguish the sentry boxes, and on the peaks of the roofs, the little stone walls that join them. Again, in line with this medallion, toward the center, in part in the shadow, the entry of the rue Copeau, where one sees several passers-by on the pavement.
>
> Exercising my right of authorship for this piece, I have indicated by my initials C.M. (with a small cross between the two letters) a house, Rue Saint-Etienne-du-Mont, 26, which I inhabited for a long period of time, where I made my suite entitled "Eaux-Fortes sur Paris." Nearby, another where I knew a little or often saw and sometimes heard a young girl with whom I was inconsiderately infatuated above all because of her strong gracious voice, which put me more than once to torture, and which had a great influence on certain events of my life, but an influence rather, alas! ill-fated.[1]

The initials LN on the house are those of Louise Neveu, whom Burty described as "a creamery-girl with whom he was infatuated and whom he wanted to marry."[2]

76.
Preparatory drawing for upper left section
Pencil with touches of red chalk
Sheet: 127 x 160 mm. (5 x 6-3/8 in.)

---

1. Ibid., pp. 92-93.   2. Philippe Burty, *Maîtres et Petits Maîtres*, Paris, 1877, p. 115.

WATERMARK: *Hal*(lines)
INSCRIPTIONS: At top in pen: *Grand dessin a une echelle un peu plus grande, completé* / *sur place* / *C.M.* / *1863*
PROVENANCE: P. Burty (L. 2071); B. B. MacGeorge (L. 394)
EXHIBITIONS: *Knoedler* N. Y. 1917, no. 138 or 139
BIBLIOGRAPHY: *Delteil,* no. 43; *DW,* no. 43
Lent by the National Gallery of Art, Rosenwald Collection (B 8698)

77.
Preparatory drawing for upper center section
Pencil with touches of red chalk
Sheet: 128 x 124 mm. (5-1/16 x 4-7/8 in.)

INSCRIPTIONS: In pencil, upper left: *H*; upper right: *Het de niveau avec G*;
center right below in pen: *Autre partie du grand* / *dessin completé sur* / *place. CM.* / *1863*
PROVENANCE: P. Burty (L. 2071); B. B. MacGeorge (L. 394)
EXHIBITIONS: *Knoedler* N.Y. 1917, no. 138 or 139
BIBLIOGRAPHY: *Delteil,* no. 43; *DW,* no. 43
Lent by the National Gallery of Art, Rosenwald Collection (B 8699)

78.
Fourth state, before the monogram and the steamship
Etching: black ink on ivory laid paper
Plate: 292 x 482 mm. (11-1/2 x 19 in.)

WATERMARK: *Hudelist*
INSCRIPTIONS: Lower left: *Imp. Pierron r. Montfaucon, 1*; extreme lower left: *Paris.*
ROCHOUX Quai de l'Horloge. 19. Lower right: *C.M. F*^*bat* *1863-64;* in bottom
margin, right: *COLLEGE HENRI IV, ou LYCÉE NAPOLÉON, Avec ses dépendances et*
constructions voisines

Cette pièce qui, à notre sens, a un coté très sérieux, indépendamment de quelques
particularités ayant trait a son exécution, que nous passerons ici sous silence, les
quelles peuvent lui prêter de l'intérêt; / n'est pas encore terminée, comme il est
facile de le voir, maintes corrections devant y être faites; mais nous offrons telles
quelles ce nombre d'épreuves (30), de cet état spécial, que nous avons dédié,
dans notre / pensée, à ces adeptes entierement devoués à la cause une et absolue
du VRAI et du BIEN, ayant pour nous quelque sympathie; (avec nos maladresses,
bien apparentes ici, non sans intérêt encore pour / la critique:) espérant que ce

présent mode d'expressions de notre manière de voir, (bizarre et fort risqué, nous le sentons, mais sincère,) trouvera accès auprès d'eux, s'ils veulent bien prendre la / peine d'interpréter les choses qui se voient figurées ci au dessus de la représentation positive, nous en reposant, pour les meilleures conclusions et parti pris subséquent, sur leur plus grande / pénétration, science, volonté et force ; et sur tout enfin sur leur plus parfait état de grâce auprès du Divin Maître qui nous guide dans les opérations de notre esprit, dans nos déterminations, ex- / auce ici bas nos voeux, et nous donne assistance pour la réalisation de nos entreprises.

Paris, ce 15 Janvier 1864.

IMPRESSIONS : Cincinnati ; London w ; Paris ; New York PL w
Lent by the Bowdoin College Museum of Art, Gift of Miss Susan Dwight Bliss
(1956.24.109)

79.
Tenth state with new letters
Etching : dark brown ink on ivory laid paper
Plate : 295 x 482 mm. (11-5/8 x 19 in.)

WATERMARK : *Hudelist*
INSCRIPTIONS : Immediately below plate : *Imp. Pierron r. Montfaucon I 1863-64;*
bottom margin, center : *VUE À VOL D'OISEAU | DU | COLLÈGE HENRI IV
ou LYCÉE NAPOLÉON | GRAND ET PETIT COLLÈGES, Avec les jardins qui en
dépendent et les constructions avoisinantes | PRISE DU SOMMET DU PANTHÉON |
PARIS DCCCLXIV;* lower right corner : *Paris, ROCHOUX Quai de l'Horloge 19*
IMPRESSIONS : Boston PL w *Hudelist* ; Brooklyn w ; Cleveland w *Hallines* ; London w ;
Mount Holyoke College w *Hallines* ; Providence cc ; Stanford University
Lent by the Davison Art Center, Wesleyan University, Middletown, Connecticut

Le Ministère de la Marine, 1865-1866   *DW* 45
The Ministry of the Marine
    Through the urging of Jules Niel, Meryon was commissioned to execute this plate for the *Société des Aquafortistes* (Society of Etchers). This enterprise, organized by Delâtre, the printer and Alfred Cadart, the publisher, (1828-1875) in 1862, issued 300 original etchings by contemporary French artists in its five year existence. It is the only association that Meryon had with this famous society that greatly contributed to the etching revival of the time.
    The Ministry, designed by Jacques-Ange Gabriel (1698-1782) in 1762-1770, one of the great works of eighteenth century architecture, stands at one side of the Place de la Concorde. In the print, great crowds of spectators and cavalry fill the

square, pointing and looking upward to the fantastic creatures that invade Paris from the sky. The large-scale sword lying on the ground may be a remembrance of Meryon's past as a naval officer,[1] but there is no clear explanation for the birds, fish, horses, and monsters that descend from above. They are the elements of pure imagination, like the visions of Bosch, of specific meaning to the artist but lost to us today. Yet to Meryon they were indispensable, and in a letter to Burty he mentioned "the somewhat large number of little figures which it was necessary to put there."[2]

The two fine preparatory drawings now mounted as one from the Fogg Art Museum (Cat. 80), detail the structures, without shading or figures. Conceived as two separate elements at this point, the drawings were transferred to the copper plate. The first state was completed by January 10, 1865; the second, soon after.[3] Addition of the sky, drawn in pencil on the proof of the second state, waited until May 9th to be completed.[4] The fourth state was not completed until January 1866.[5]

It should now be evident that Meryon was working very slowly on this plate. At the start of 1866 he had been laboring over this for a year, and had not yet printed anything but trial impressions. Dr. Paul Gachet (1828-1909), remembered today for his friendship with Van Gogh, treated Meryon at Charenton and wrote that this print "preoccupied and distressed Meryon very much."[6] It was published in August 1866, and was his last work of a Parisian subject.

80.
Study for the print: two drawings mounted together as one
Pencil on white paper
144 x 136 mm. (5-11/16 x 5-3/16 in.)

PROVENANCE: F. Seymour Haden (initials lower right on each sheet)
EXHIBITIONS: *Grolier Club, N. Y. 1898*, no. 122

---

1. His father sent Meryon a sword around 1845-46, and he replied: "It is an exceptionally handsome weapon, too handsome for me; but after all, you have presented it to me with so much goodness that I keep it as a truly cherished remembrance. It will certainly be the [nicest] ornament of my room; I will hang it above my bed. . . . I will have two precious objects in my house: your sword and my mother's small clock." *Paris 1968*, no. 365.
2. Copy of a letter by Meryon in his own hand, dated January 12, 1865, in the Toledo Museum of Art.
3. Of the three known impressions of this state, two are dated and signed by Meryon (London, New York PL), and the third (Paris) is a first proof before any burnishing of the plate. An impression of the second state is dated eight days later, according to *DW*, 1924.   4. The New York Public Library now owns a signed and dated proof of the second state, with pencil indications for the sky and figures; another signed by Meryon 9 *Mai* / *Epreuve etat* / *CM*, is in the Metropolitan Museum, New York (17.78.16).   5. *Delteil*, 1907, mentions a proof with this date inscribed by Meryon in the MacGeorge Collection.   6. Letter to A. Bouvenne, quoted in Bailly-Herzberg, 1972, *L'Eau-forte de Peintre*, I, p. 150.

BIBLIOGRAPHY: *Delteil*, 1907, no. 45; *DW*, 1924, no. 45
Lent by the Fogg Art Museum, Harvard University, Cambridge, Massachusetts.
Gift of the Estate of William and Frances White Emerson (1957.171)

81.
Fifth state, completed and with the artist's monogram at lower center, but before the letters
Etching and drypoint: black ink on white laid paper
Plate: 168 x 143 mm. (6-5/8 x 5-5/8 in.)

WATERMARK: —*Caner*—(?)
INSCRIPTIONS: At bottom: monogram
IMPRESSIONS: Amsterdam w; Baltimore; Boston w *Aqua Fortistes*; Bowdoin College w; Cambridge (Fitzwilliam) w; Chicago w *Aqua Fortistes*; Cincinnati; Cleveland w *Aqua Fortistes*; Detroit; London w; Minneapolis, New York w; New York PL w; Toledo
Lent by the Philadelphia Museum of Art: William S. Pilling Collection (33-72-1459)

Rue Pirouette aux Halles, 1860   DW 49
Rue Pirouette, near the Markets
   The etching was made from a drawing by Louis-Marie Laurence (1811-1886), a minor etcher-draughtsman who also did city views. Burty and Meryon agree that this marks a new stylistic phase in the Meryon's work. The artist admitted that "the execution here is very minute; for the first time I used the burin more than I was accustomed to," adding that "it is necessary to use a magnifying glass to recognize certain details of the various states."[1] There can be little doubt that Meryon was fascinated with the smallest details in his own prints; it seems certain that he worked with the aid of a magnifying glass, at least in the late 1850s and in the 1860s. Every small figure, incident, window, sign and moulding had meaning for him.
   Burty later suggested that Meryon worked from Laurence's drawing because he was "at that time prey to melancholy," and "dreaded to work in the streets." Yet Meryon wrote that "in completing it on the spot, I had to enlarge it a little."[2]
   Laurence's original drawing is not available to us today. Meryon's drawing, now at Pittsburgh (Cat. 82) may have been traced from Laurence's drawing onto this sheet. Only the outlines of forms appear in the pencil lines. Meryon then drew the

---

1. *Burty I,* 1863, p. 531; *Mes Observations,* no. 23.   2. *Burty and Huish,* 1879, p. 43; *Mes Observations,* no. 23.

outlines of shadows in red, and numbered each shadow area one through four to indicate the value of the shadow. This is an important change from the *Eaux-Fortes sur Paris,* where shadows were introduced in the etching stage and were not so precisely set forth in the drawings. It is symptomatic of Meryon's development away from spontaneity toward an even greater fixation on precision, inseparable from his mental troubles.

Meryon printed the first three states himself, when the plate was least worn. The third state (Cat. 83) from the Rosenwald Collection was printed in twenty impressions, with the initials "C.M. et L." on the chimney at right, representing Meryon and Laurence, or, possibly, Meryon and Louise (see *Collège Henri IV,* Cat. 79). Later states were handled by Delâtre.

82.
Preparatory drawing, with outlines of shadows in red and numbers to indicate values of shadow
Pencil with touches of red crayon on gray paper
151 x 97 mm. (5-15/16 x 3-13/16 in.)

INSCRIPTIONS: In pencil lower left by CM: *la lumiere en plein d— burin (un peu de disette)*
PROVENANCE: J. Niel (*DW*); H. Destailleur (*DW*); B. B. MacGeorge (L. 394); Knoedler, N. Y. 1917
EXHIBITIONS: *Knoedler, N. Y. 1917,* no. 140
BIBLIOGRAPHY: *DW,* 1924, no. 49
Lent by the Museum of Art, Carnegie Institute, Pittsburgh (17.30.1)

83.
Third state
Etching: brown ink on gray paper
Plate: 155 x 115 mm. (6-1/8 x 4-9/16 in.)

INSCRIPTIONS: *RUE PIROUETTE | 1860* in lower margin; *C.M. et L* on the sheathing of a chimney in the right background
IMPRESSIONS: Baltimore w; Boston w; Cambridge (Fitzwilliam) w *Hudelist*; Chicago c; Cleveland w; London w; New York PL
Lent by the National Gallery of Art, Rosenwald Collection (B 9037)

L'Ancien Louvre, d'après Zéeman, 1865-1866   *DW 53*
The Old Louvre, after Zeeman
The Print Department of the Louvre (Chalcographie du Louvre) often commissioned etched or engraved copies of popular works of art in the museum.

This etching reproduces the painting (dated 1651) by the Dutch artist Reynier Nooms, called Zeeman. Meryon greatly admired Zeeman, who was thought to have been a sailor. He dedicated the *Eaux-Fortes sur Paris* to Zeeman, and in fact began his printmaking career by making copies of Zeeman's etchings (*DW* 9-16).

Burty arranged this commission for Meryon.[1] The preparatory drawing, now at Bowdoin College (Cat. 84), is softer and weaker than his earlier work, the crackling vitality of line is missing, and the figures appear labored. Work on the plate began in August 1865, with the first state. However, five months elapsed before completion of the third state in January 1866.[2] An impression of the fourth state, now in the Rosenwald Collection, was exhibited in the Salon of 1866; another impression is dated April 3rd (Private collection, New Hampshire). The only editions were printed and published by the Chalcographie du Louvre in the last two states, some without the letter, shown here from Pittsburgh (Cat. 85), and a vast number, still available, with the inscriptions.

84.
Preparatory study
Pencil on ivory laid paper
114 x 257 mm. (4-1/2 x 10-1/8 in.)

WATERMARK: *Hudelist*
PROVENANCE: B. B. MacGeorge (L. 394)
EXHIBITIONS: *Knoedler, N. Y. 1917,* no. 141
BIBLIOGRAPHY: *DW,* 1924, no. 53
Lent by the Bowdoin College Museum of Art, Gift of Miss Susan Dwight Bliss
(1956.24.227a)

85.
Fifth state, as completed. One of a set printed before the insertion of the letters, as published by the Louvre Print Department
Etching and drypoint: dark brown ink on white wove paper
Plate: 138 x 232 mm. (5-7/16 x 9-1/8 in.)

PROVENANCE: Chalcographie du Louvre (L. 1695); A. W. Thibaudeau (L. 2412); B. B. MacGeorge (L. 394)

---

1. See Burty's letter to Comte de Nieuwerkerke, Director General of the Imperial Museums, February 6, 1865; *Paris 1968,* no. 430.   2. Signed and dated proof in New York, others in Chicago, New York PL, and Washington. The second state is known in one impression, at Washington, with the sky drawn in pencil; only one impression is known of the first state at London.

Porte d'un Ancien Couvent à Bourges, 1851   DW 54
Doorway of an Old Convent, Bourges

Through the early 1850s, Meryon planned a set of views of Bourges to parallel
his Paris suite. This old medieval city attracted the artist, with its "curious
remnants of the middle ages."[1] As with Paris, antiquarian interest drew him to old
streets and picturesque houses. He visited Bourges in 1850 and 1851,[2] where he
made numerous drawings.[3] He prepared model title pages for the proposed set
in 1852, and wrote to the Minister of the Interior to offer the set in 1854.[4] In the
letter, he enclosed a proof of this etching which he described as unfinished; in
Mes Observations he stated that he wanted to complete it.[5]

An impression of the first state in Paris is dated by Meryon in 1851, the
probable date of the preparatory drawing, now also at Paris (A.C. 8528).[6] This
print is unusually rare; of the three states described, only eight impressions are
known today. All are of superb quality due to the perfect condition of the plate,
almost all are on japan paper, as is the case with the unique proof of the second
state (Cat. 86) from Toledo.

86.
Second state
Etching on japan paper
Plate: 168 x 111 mm. (6-5/8 x 4-3/8 in.)

INSCRIPTIONS: Monogram at lower left corner
Lent by the Toledo Museum of Art (25.55)

La Rue des Toiles à Bourges, 1853   DW 55
"A somber and crooked street," wrote Burty, "in which the houses are of the
most pure style of the fourteenth and fifteenth centuries."[7]

Meryon wrote to his father in 1853 about the print:

---

1. In a letter to his father, August 13, 1854; cited in *Drost*, 1964, "Documents Nouveaux," p. 239, note 55.
2. Ibid, p. 239.   3. Most of the drawings of Bourges are identified and illustrated in Jean Jenny, "Eaux-fortes
et Dessins de Charles Meryon relatifs à Bourges," *Cahiers d'archéologie et d'histoire du Berry* no. 10, (1967), p. 3
and *DW*, 1924 under the entry on views of Bourges, between numbers 53 and 54.   4. The titles and letter
appear in *Delteil*, 1907 and *DW*, 1924 under the entry on views of Bourges, between numbers 53 and 54.
5. *Mes Observations*, no. 55.   6. Reproduced in *Delteil*, 1907, no. 54.   7. *Burty II*, 1863, p. 85.

The composition of this piece has cost me much more pain than one could ever have believed as I have never made use of a Daguerreotype until now, for many reasons, the acquisition of the necessary materials has demanded of me both time and work. Add to this that all the lower parts of the houses were modern and by consequence strongly dissimilar to the upper parts which date from many centuries.[1]

This is one of the first shreds of evidence to link Meryon with photography, although it is unclear whether he took the daguerreotype himself, or just worked from it. He wrote to Burty in the 1860s that he had combined details from various houses for this subject, in order to insure a true medieval character.[2] That he thought of himself as a connoisseur of such architecture is clear.

Only the final drawing for the print is known, now at Chicago (Cat. 87). It is mounted with its verso up, which is also drawn to correct some details and make minor alterations. Meryon drew the subject as it would finally appear in a printed proof, then reversed the final drawing to work on the plate. This solved the problem of working in mirror image at any given time, and may have resulted, in the sixth state, from his contact with cameras.

The finished etching, (Cat. 88) from Pittsburgh, differs chiefly in the addition of a tree at right, smoke from the chimneys and details of staffage. The stronger shading that appears in the etching once again transforms the character of the work—the narrow street is darker and the walls of houses loom even more over the tiny inhabitants.

The first two states are only for trial, and Meryon seems to have printed a fair number of impressions in each state, as often on greenish paper as not. The plate was published in large numbers in 1863, to accompany the first appreciation of Meryon's prints in English.[3]

87.
Final preparatory drawing for the print
Pencil on ivory laid paper
222 x 132 mm. (8-3/4 x 5-3/16 in.)

INSCRIPTIONS: Lower right: 26
PROVENANCE: B. B. MacGeorge (L. 394)

---

1. Letter of June 20, 1853, quoted in *Paris 1968*, no. 744. 2. ". . . the lower parts [of the houses] had . . . been so disfigured by modern restorations that I obtained from other quarters of the town details which would best accord with the upper stories," quoted in *Burty and Huish*, 1879, p. 76. It is interesting that he omits the ground level of the houses completely in another drawing of a similar street in Bourges, in the British Museum, London. (1890-10-13-21). 3. Philip G. Hamerton, "Modern Etching in France," *The Fine Arts Quarterly Review* II, (1864) p. 69.

EXHIBITIONS: *Knoedler, N. Y. 1917*, no. 142
BIBLIOGRAPHY: *Delteil, 1907*, no. 55(?); *DW*, 1924, no. 55
Lent by the Art Institute of Chicago: The Stickney Collection (1920.2557)

88.
Sixth state, only minor differences in the figures mark the states in this print
Etching and drypoint: brown in on gray (imitation) china paper
Plate: 212 x 117 mm. (8-3/8 x 4-5/8 in.)

PROVENANCE: J. J. Heywood (Wright inscription verso); B. B. MacGeorge (L. 394)
IMPRESSIONS: Washington g
Lent by the Museum of Art, Carnegie Institute, Pittsburgh (17.30.14)

Ancienne Habitation à Bourges, 1852-1860   *DW 56*
Old Dwelling-place, Bourges
  A fine half-timbered house remaining from the late Middle Ages, this was by tradition "La Maison du Musicien," ("the house of a musician"), with its corner post carved in the form of a flageolet.
  "I have a particular regard for this plate," wrote Meryon. "It is interesting not only on account of the architectural originality of the building itself, but also because of the exactness with which I have reproduced it. I etched this plate for Monsieur Niel, who possesses the drawing for it which I made on the spot."[1]
  The original drawing, dated 1852, is at Williamstown (Cat. 89). The etching follows this model except for the figures, further delineation of houses, definition of shadows and insertion of the sky. Each of these additions occur in the early states of the etching, as if in turn. The proof of the third state, from the Boston Public Library (Cat. 90) is one of only three and is finished in all parts but the two houses at the rear and the modelling of smoke and sky. This could be considered a trial proof, as is the case in each of the earlier two states.[2] The fifth and final state, with the title, was published in large edition in the *Gazette des Beaux-Arts* in 1860. Perhaps it was Niel, recognizing the striking evocation of an old city in this subject, who brought it to the attention of this famous journal for publication.

89.
Preparatory drawing
Pencil on laid paper
264 x 148 mm. (10-3/8 x 5-13/16 in.)

---

1. *Mes Observations*, no. 57.   2. The first four states are trials, in which details are resolved leading to the completed fifth state. Known impressions: first state, Washington; second state, London; third state, Boston and Boston PL; fourth state, London, Paris and Pittsburgh.

INSCRIPTIONS: Inscribed by the artist with pen and brown ink at bottom right:
à Monsieur Niel / dessin fait sur-place, à / Bourges - an 52 / C. Meryon; and with pencil
above: *R. Bourbon. Chez M. / B. . . . (word crossed out) - Une / porte - / cheminée à . . .
/ normale - Rue Paradis / R. Bourbonnoux 23 / Ins. de maison / petite porte. R. Bourb.*
PROVENANCE: J. Niel; J. J. Heywood (*DW*); B. B. MacGeorge (L. 394);
Knoedler, N. Y. (bought by R. S. Clark 1917)
EXHIBITIONS: *Grolier Club, N. Y. 1898*, no. 117(?); *Knoedler, N. Y. 1917*, no. 143;
Williamstown 1966, no. 248
BIBLIOGRAPHY: *Delteil, 1907*, no. 56; *Bradley, 1917*, p. 247 (repr.); *DW, 1924*,
no. 56; E. H. Begemann et al., *Drawings from the Clark Art Institute*, New Haven,
1964, no. 248 (pl. 94)
Lent by the Sterling and Francine Clark Art Institute, Williamstown,
Massachusetts (1854)

90.
Third state, complete with the initials of the artist at lower left
Etching and drypoint: dark brown ink on ivory laid paper
Plate: 241 x 139 mm. (9-1/2 x 5-1/2 in.)

WATERMARK: *Hallines*
INSCRIPTIONS: Lower left corner: *CM*
IMPRESSIONS: Boston w; New York PL w
Lent by the Print Department, Boston Public Library

Couverture du Voyage à la Nouvelle Zélande, 1866   DW 63
Cover for Voyage to New Zealand
   By the time he etched this cover, Meryon had already produced most of the
etchings for this proposed set of subjects from his voyage to the Pacific on the
corvette *Rhin* in 1842-1846. His original drawings from the 1840s were reworked
for these prints. The full title reads: "Various Printed Pieces, the collection,
winnings and spoil from cruising or hunting, made at anchor and at sea during the
voyage to New Zealand, 1842 to 1846 on the ship *Rhin* under the orders of Captain
A. Bérard (died Vice-Admiral in 1852), Commandant of the station at Akaroa,
Banks Peninsula."
   Meryon made numerous drawings during the voyage, studies of places visited,
natives, birds, fish, trees, native sculpture, and boats among other things.[1] Burty

1. A number of these drawings are catalogued and reproduced in *Paris 1968*, nos. 92-97, 776-799, and 802-809.
Details of the voyage are discussed at some length in the section "Voyage de Circumnavigation de la corvette
le 'Rhin'" in *Paris 1968*, nos. 1-108. See also Sinclair H. Hitchings, "Meryon's Voyage and Vision of the
Pacific," *Print Collector's Newsletter* I, no. 5, (1970) pp. 102-104.

commented on the great number of drawings from the Pacific that Meryon had in his possession in 1863.[1]

The first etching related to the Pacific voyage was *Le Pilote de Tonga* (*DW* 64) in 1856. By 1863, Meryon was running short of fresh inspiration and funds, existing on commissions from friends. The height of his great creative power was in the first half of the 1850s, slowly dispelled by the anguish of mental decline. Thus he turned to his own happy experiences of almost twenty years earlier for the subjects for a new group of etchings, completed in 1863-1866.

The original drawing for *Couverture du Voyage à la Nouvelle Zélande,* once in the MacGeorge Collection, is now at Toledo.[2] Meryon made seven states of the etching before he completed it in the eighth state, shown here in a fine impression from Toledo (Cat. 91).

91.
Eighth state, with the title. The final and published state
Etching: black ink on brown paper
Plate: 154 x 238 mm. (6 x 9-3/8 in.)

INSCRIPTIONS: *Voyage à la Nouvelle Zélande.* . . . Monogram in lower center
IMPRESSIONS: Boston 1 bl, 1 br; London 1 bl, 1 br; New York br
Lent by the Toledo Museum of Art (21.183)

Le Pilote de Tonga, 1856   *DW* 64
The Pilot of Tonga
This was the first etched souvenir of Meryon's travels in the Pacific, which he dated in the plate as 1842-1846. It is a "song in prose," as Burty wrote,[3] to recall the native pilot in the Tonga Islands (Cat. 92, Toledo).

The border, in red and black, imitates block-printed fabrics of the South Pacific.[4]

> We were leaving Tonga on a ship of war; there came the pilot
> in a frail canoe.
>
> He is almost completely nude. Strong and agile, in one jump
> he is on board; he goes straight to the captain and salutes him
> with dignity.
>
> The ship opens its sails to the wind; briskly pushed by the breeze
> that blows them, it enters into the narrow and dangerous passage!
>
> Standing on a bench on the watch, his head high, his eye
> attentive, the skillful pilot indicates by gesture the route of the

---

1. *Burty II,* 1863, p. 85.   2. *Rogers,* 1963, p. 16, reproduced.   3. *Burty II,* 1863, p. 85.   4. This was first noted in *Paris 1968,* no. 753.

ship that plays in the reefs! His stance is noble and proud:
everything in him denotes assurance. His large chest, his bronzed
complexion, shines in the sun like a bronzed buckle, his long
hair floats in the wind. . . .

On board all is at rest; officers and sailors admire him in silence. . .
And the ship sails, sails on always . . .
But the channel widens . . . already a large swell
splashes under the prow . . .

Hurrah! Valiant Pilot! Hurrah!
The passage is free!

Pursue your course, O beautiful ship; before us opens
The Ocean!
Thanks to you pilot of Tonga!

92.
Second state, complete
Etching: red and black ink on white laid paper
Plate: 203 x 144 mm. (8 x 5-5/8 in.)

WATERMARK: Fragment of a coat of arms
INSCRIPTIONS: Along bottom: *Souvenir de voyage MDCCCXLIII - VI . . . A. Delâtre
Imp. rue Fg. St Jacques No. 81*

Le Pilote de Tonga

Nous partions de Tonga sur un
navire de guerre; vient le pilote dans sa
frêle pirogue.

Il est presque complètement nu. Fort et
agile, en un saut il est à bord; il va droit
au Commandant et le salue dignement.

Le navire ouvre ses voiles au vent,
vivement poussé par la brise qui les gon-
fle, il donne dans
l'étroite et dangereuse Passe!

Debout sur le banc de quart, la tête hau-
te, l'oeil attentif, l'habile pilote indique du ges-
te la route du navire que se joue dans les ré-
cifs! Son attitude est noble et fière; tout chez

95

lui dénote l'assurance. Sa large poitrine, de
teinte basanée, brille au Soleil comme un bou-
clier d'airain ; ses longs cheveux flottent au
vent . . .

A bord tout se tait : Officiers et matelots
l'admirent en silence . . .

Et le navire marche, marche toujours . . .
Mais la voie s'agrandit . . . Déjà la
houle du large clapote sous la proue . . .

Houra! vaillant pilote! Houra!
La Passe est franche!

Poursuis ta course, ô beau navire ; devant nous s'ouvre
l'Océan!
A toi merci pilote de Tonga!

IMPRESSIONS : Boston w ; Cleveland w ; London w ; Paris w
Lent by the Toledo Museum of Art (24.36)

Océanie, Pêche aux Palmes, 1863   *DW* 68
Oceania, Fishing near Palm trees

The full title describes "fishing near small islands with palm trees" at Uvea in
the Wallis Islands, which lie between Fiji and Western Samoa. Native fishers
stand in the water with a line of nets (Cat. 93, Pittsburgh). Meryon described the
scene himself :

> Some natives, most of their bodies submerged, descend into sea,
> holding open baskets . . . formed of branches or fronds of coconut
> palms, held together at the bottom, to receive the fish that were
> taken in and imprisoned there, while others [fishermen] chase it
> in front of them. At the right, a sort of oval formed of coconut
> palms . . . and other trees on a rock; at the back, an island (Fayoa, if
> I am not mistaken); at the left on the horizon, a rock, surging out
> of the sea, on a platform that serves as a base . . . . In the right corner,
> underneath the little island, one can distinguish a small canoe,
> of a form peculiar to these islands.[1]

The original study for the etching is now in the Art Institute of Chicago.[2] The
etching was printed by the commercial publisher Pierron, and exhibited at the
Salon of 1863.

---

1. *Mes Observations*, no. 63 and 64.   2. *Paris 1968*, no. 758.

93.
Fourth state, with the letters, as completed. A fine, early impression with even
plate tone
Etching and drypoint: reddish brown ink on ivory laid paper
Plate: 116 x 293 mm. (4-9/16 x 11-9/16 in.)

WATERMARK: *Hudelist*
INSCRIPTIONS: In margin at lower left: *C.M. ft 1863*; at lower right: *Imp. Pierron r
Montfaucon 1 Paris*
PROVENANCE: J. J. Heywood (Wright inscription verso); B. B. MacGeorge (L. 394)
IMPRESSIONS: Amsterdam w; Baltimore; Boston 2 *Hudelist*; Cambridge
(Fitzwilliam) *Hallines*; Cleveland 2; London; Smith College w *Hallines,* w
Hudelist; Toledo; Wesleyan University w
Lent by the Museum of Art, Carnegie Institute, Pittsburgh (17.30.18)

Presqu'île de Banks, Pointe des Charbonniers, Akaroa, 1863   *DW* 69
Banks Peninsula, Colliers Point, Akaroa (New Zealand)
   Meryon's ship spent most of 1843 based at Akaroa, where he made other
drawings that would result in prints in the 1860s (*DW* 70, 71, and 72). He wrote:

> This view is one of those which we had in the same wind direction
> as our anchorage, which we occupied for a long time, the same
> where the several dwellings forming the French part of the base
> are formed.
> Here I enlivened this subject with sailors or colonists fishing, in the
> middle of the net communally employed with what one calls seine
> fishing. A Gentleman and a Lady follow this operation at the same
> time that they observe the countryside spreading out in all
> directions in the distance. If the hills seem arid, I have drawn
> them badly, because most are, on the contrary, heavily wooded;
> the summits alone are covered with grass or rocks, those of various
> forms often set in the earth in a picturesque way.[1]

   The drawing made on the site in about 1843 is at the Minneapolis Institute of
Arts (Cat. 94), much more general in style than Meryon's later work. The study for
the etching, at Toledo (Cat. 95), made in 1863, is much sharper and more detailed.
The rich detail is very different from the more atmospheric quality of the
Minneapolis sheet, although the Toledo drawing is the final study for the etching,
which was made in the same year.

---

1. *Mes Observations,* nos. 63 and 64.

The etching itself (Cat. 96) at Wesleyan University, sharper yet than the preparatory drawing, is shown here in a superb impression of the fourth and last state from Burty's own collection.

94.
Original study, made on the site
Pencil
255 x 470 mm. (10-1/16 x 18-1/2 in.)

PROVENANCE: M. Salicis (inscription verso); B. B. MacGeorge (L. 394)
EXHIBITIONS: *Knoedler, N. Y. 1917*, no. 148
BIBLIOGRAPHY: *Delteil*, 1907, no. 69; *DW*, 1924, no. 69
Lent by the Minneapolis Institute of Arts, Gift of H. V. Jones (19.2)

95.
Final study for the etching
Pencil on ivory laid paper, squared for transfer
139 x 317 mm. (5-1/2 x 12-1/2 in.)

WATERMARK: *Hudelist*
INSCRIPTIONS: In pen and ink, lower center: *La Pointe-des-Charbonniers | d'apres mon dessin original fait à Akaroa, Nelle. Zelande | C.M.*
PROVENANCE: P. Burty (L. 2071, on old mat); B. B. MacGeorge (L. 394, on old mat); C. Dowdeswell (L. 690); Knoedler, N. Y. 1923
EXHIBITIONS: *Knoedler, N. Y. 1917*, no. 149; *Toledo 1963*
BIBLIOGRAPHY: *Delteil*, 1907, no. 69; *DW*, 1924, no. 69; *Grigaut*, 1950, p. 234, no. 17; *Rogers TMN*, 1963, p. 43; *Rogers*, 1963, p. 17 (repr.)
Lent by the Toledo Museum of Art (22.53)

96.
Fourth state with the lettering
Etching: black ink on ivory laid paper
Plate: 157 x 326 mm. (6-3/16 x 12-7/8 in.)

INSCRIPTIONS: In plate at lower left: *C.M. del et sculp. 1863*; lower right: *Pierron Imp. r Montfaucon I*; center: *NOUVELLE ZÉLANDE   Presqu'il de BANKS. 1845 | Pointe dite des Charbonniers à AKAROA. Pêche à la Seine*
PROVENANCE: P. Burty (L. 413)
IMPRESSIONS: Baltimore; Boston; Cleveland; London

Lent by the Davison Art Center, Wesleyan University, Middletown, Connecticut

Case abandonnée, Akaroa, Nelle. Zélande, 1843
Abandoned Hut, Akaroa, New Zealand
   Like the drawing of the bay of Akaroa at Minneapolis (Cat. 94), this drawing was made on the spot by Meryon during his visit to New Zealand in 1843. It is an excellent example of his early style, already concerned with the bright light of the Pacific. This interest in light and shadow evolved subtly from the Pacific drawings into Meryon's art of the late 1840s, as seen in the Yale drawing of Notre-Dame (Cat. 67) and into the still more dramatic *Eaux-Fortes sur Paris* of the 1850s.

97.
Study of an abandoned hut, Akaroa, New Zealand
Pencil on white wove paper
226 x 311 mm. (8-7/8 x 12-1/4 in.)

INSCRIPTIONS: In pencil, at left: *Akaroa. Fev. 43*; center: *Case abandonée (Nelle. Zelande)*; right: *C.M.f.*
PROVENANCE: F. Carrington, N. Y. 1923
EXHIBITIONS: *Toledo 1963*
BIBLIOGRAPHY: *Grigaut,* 1950, p. 239, no. 26
Lent by the Toledo Museum of Art (23.3096)

La Chaumière du Colon Vieux-Soldat, 1866   *DW 72*
Cottage of the Old Soldier-Colonist
   A charming and very small subject at Akaroa, New Zealand, presumably made from a drawing done on the spot in 1845.
   The copper plate, still in remarkably good condition, is preserved in the Toledo Museum of Art (Cat. 98). A fine impression, also from Toledo (Cat. 99), is exhibited.

98.
Copper plate, third state
79 x 76 mm. (3-3/16 x 3 in.)

INSCRIPTIONS: *LA CHAUMIÈRE DU COLON VIEUX-SOLDAT | À AKAROA (Nelle ZÉLANDE) | 1845 | C.M. 1866 Pierron Imp^r.*
Lent by the Toledo Museum of Art

99

99.
Third state
Etching and drypoint: black ink on white laid paper
Plate: 79 x 76 mm. (3-3/16 x 3 in.)

WATERMARK: *1800*
INSCRIPTIONS: In plate: *LA CHAUMIÈRE DU COLON VIEUX-SOLDAT | A AKAROA (NELLE - ZELANDE) | 1845 | C.M. 1866 | Pierron Imp.*
IMPRESSIONS: Baltimore; Cleveland w; London w; New York PL; Paris w; Toledo 2 w
Lent by the Toledo Museum of Art (23.3087B)

San Francisco, 1856-1857   DW 73

 This superb panorama was commissioned by François-Alfred Pioche and Jules B. Bayerque, two French entrepreneurs in San Francisco whose business was real estate speculation. Allegorical figures of Abundance and Work flank their portraits over the title. This unusually large etching was intended to serve as a high-class souvenir of their adopted city.[1]

 The view was based on five daguerreotypes taken on the site and sent to Meryon in Paris. He spent more than a year working on the drawings and the plate, starting by March 1856. He wrote his father that it would take five or six months and was very picturesque. He continued to work on the subject, but in September he complained to his father that he was obliged to make one large drawing as the daguerreotypes did not match in perspective.[2]

> It was a tiresome labor. The materials on which I had to work
> consisted of *un panorama Daguerre* on plates, composed of five little
> square views, made successively, possibly on the same day, at
> different hours in any case, since one end-piece was lighted from
> one side, whereas the other was lighted from the opposite side.
> Thus, to avoid the fatigue that results from the glare on the plates,
> they had the kindness to give me also some partial views recorded
> on paper.[3]

---

1. For a complete discussion of the commissioners and the city of San Francisco at this period, as well as Meryon's print, see the excellent articles by Lloyd L. Rollins, "Charles Meryon and His 'Vue De San Francisco,'" *Quarterly of the Society of California Pioneers* IX, no. 2, (1932) pp. 97-107, and O. J. Rothrock, "The San Francisco of Alfred Pioche and Charles Meryon," *Princeton University Library Chronicle* (1973), pp. 1-25, where the paper photographic enlargements were first published.   2. Letters of March 26 and September, 1856, in *Paris 1968,* no. 764.   3. *Burty I,* 1863, p. 530.

The original daguerreotypes are unknown today, but paper albumen prints from collodion negatives made from them belong to the Art Institute of Chicago (Cat. 100). They describe a view from Russian Hill to Rincon Hill, with Alcatraz Island at left and Yerba Buena Island at center. Meryon touched up these paper prints with pencil, restating the lines of the far side of the bay.

To judge from the tone of his letters, these paper enlargements must have followed much arduous and unrewarding preliminary work on Meryon's part. Using these photographic prints, he probably made a full-size tracing. Specific details of staffage, shading and the cartouche were then drawn separately. A study of the pasture at left (Cat. 101) also from Chicago, was traced in outline from the enlargements, then drawn to illustrate figures, foliage and animals. The cartouche and figures were drawn in several studies.[1] Most charming of all are studies of tiny horses and riders from Williamstown (Cat. 102).

All these elements were transferred to a final master drawing traced from the paper enlargements and from the individual studies of Meryon's insertions. This is the drawing in the Stickney Collection, Art Institute of Chicago (09.294); from this, Meryon prepared the etching plate.

The first state of the print follows this drawing, and like the drawing has only one portrait medallion at center, that of Alfred Pioche.[2] The second state, as described by Delteil and Wright may not exist, as no impressions can be located and the description may in fact refer to the impression now at Yale (Cat. 103). This is Delteil and Wright's third state, a unique proof with the portrait of Bayerque scratched out of the printed sheet. One could surmise, therefore, that Bayerque may have been a latecomer to the commission of the etching.

This etching marks the point when Meryon's art began to trouble him increasingly, as indicated by the great length of time expended on it and the painful and detailed correspondence about his problems. He wrote to his father in London of the anxiety this plate had caused, the enormous time in preparation, culminating with "the day when I poured the treacherous liquid [the acid] on the plate, what emotion did I not feel! It was almost a question of life or death for me! At last, thanks to a kind and extraordinary fate, it must be agreed, the result

---

1. The Chicago sheet was later mounted recto down by Meryon, for transfer to the plate. Of the other drawings, two sheets of studies for the cartouche are at Chicago (09.293 and 09.294); a study for the figure of Abundance and architectural details is at Williamstown; see E. Haverkamp-Begemann et al., *Drawings from the Clark Art Institute*, New Haven, 1964, no. 256, reproduced. The complete study of the cartouche and allegorical figures is in the New York Public Library, reproduced by O. Rothrock, 1973, "San Francisco," Fig. 8. A study for the man standing in the doorway of the house at near right is also at Chicago.   2. Only one impression is to be found today, at the Art Institute of Chicago (09.304), inscribed by Meryon 1ere *épreuve d'essai*.

seemed to surpass my expectation. . . . However, for a moment, I was gravely upset. . . ."[1]

This period coincided with the onset of his initial bout of serious mental illness that culminated in his admission to the asylum at Charenton (May 1858) about a year after the last state was published. The strange imagery of birds and skies had begun to haunt him, and in 1863 he wrote:

> At the time when I executed this print, I had the idea, to avoid the break in continuity that exists in the center, to represent there fire, with flames and smoke reaching toward the sky, and birds of prey whirling above; but rushed as I was, I was not able to carry out this idea.[2]

100.
Five paper photographic enlargements of panorama of San Francisco, taken from five original daguerreotypes

PROVENANCE: M. Salicis (Salicis Sale, Christie, London, no. 28); H. Mansfield
EXHIBITIONS: *Grolier Club, N. Y. 1898*, no. 107a; *Chicago, 1911*, no. 112a
BIBLIOGRAPHY: *DW*, 1924, no. 73; O. J. Rothrock, "The San Francisco of Alfred Pioche and Charles Meryon," *Princeton University Library Chronicle* (1973) p. 1 ff., Fig. 4
Lent by the Art Institute of Chicago: The Stickney Collection (1909.290)

101.
Study for pasture and figures, left side
Pencil on tracing paper, mounted with verso up
208 x 259 mm. (8-3/16 x 10-3/16 in.)

PROVENANCE: H. Mansfield (L. 1342)
EXHIBITIONS: *Grolier Club, N. Y. 1898*, no. 107c; *Chicago 1911*, no. 112c
Lent by the Art Institute of Chicago: The Stickney Collection (1909.291)

102.
Study of horses and riders, figures at far right in the etching
Pencil on tissue paper
99 x 60 mm. (3-15/16 x 2-3/8 in.)

---

1. Letter by Meryon to Burty, 1961, quoted in *Burty I*, 1863, p. 529.   2. *Mes Observations*, no. 21.

PROVENANCE: B. B. MacGeorge (L. 394); Knoedler, N. Y. (bought by R. S. Clark 1917)
EXHIBITIONS: *Knoedler, N. Y. 1917*, no. 152 or 153; *Williamstown 1966*, no. 257
BIBLIOGRAPHY: *DW*, 1924, no. 73; E. H. Begemann et al., *Drawings from the Clark Art Institute*, New Haven, 1964, no. 257
Lent by the Sterling and Francine Clark Art Institute, Williamstown, Massachusetts (1530)

103.
Third state with left medallion scratched out
Etching and drypoint: brown ink on ivory laid paper
Plate: 240 x 998 mm. (9-1/2 x 39-1/4 in.)

WATERMARK: fragment of a Crown
INSCRIPTIONS: On plaque beside left medallion: *J.J.B.*; beside right medallion: *A.P.*; in center: *San Francisco*; below: *MDCCCLV*
PROVENANCE: J. J. Heywood; B. B. MacGeorge (L. 394)
Lent by the Yale University Art Gallery, Gift of Edward B. Greene, B.A. 1900 (1931.70)

Casimir Le Conte, 1856   *DW* 77
    The full identity of this distinguished-looking man is not established. Probably a private commission, this etching was made after a drawing in the style of Ingres by Gustave Boulanger (1824-1888). Meryon noted that he "copied most faithfully as possible the original drawing which was very beautiful: and had to overcome, in the interpretation, some great difficulties, as the style was not that of my own."[1]
    The original drawing by Boulanger is not known today, although the plate, still well-preserved, is in the Boston Public Library (Cat. 104). An unusually fine impression from the plate, at Pittsburgh (Cat. 105) is exhibited, inscribed by the artist as proof for printing.

104.
Copper plate
343 x 267 mm. (13-1/2 x 10-1/2 in.)

INSCRIPTIONS: *C. Meryon. del aqua-forte / 1856 d'apres G.B.*
PROVENANCE: A. Delâtre; E. Delâtre
Lent by the Print Department, Boston Public Library

---

1. *Mes Observations*, no. 76.

105.
Second (last) state, as completed
Etching and drypoint: brown ink on brown (imitation) chine collé
Plate: 325 x 249 mm. (12-13/16 x 9-13/16 in.)

INSCRIPTIONS: In plate lower right: *C. Meryon del aqua forte | 1856 d'apres G.B.*;
lower right margin, by the artist: *Bon a tirer | Casimir Le Conte*
PROVENANCE: P. Burty (L. 413); J. J. Heywood (Wright inscription verso);
B. B. MacGeorge (L. 394)
IMPRESSIONS: Amsterdam j; London vellum and counterproof; New York w;
Paris 1 w, 1 chine; Private collection, Conn. w; Toledo w
Lent by the Museum of Art, Carnegie Institute, Pittsburgh (17.30.4)

Portrait of Armand Guéraud, with Frame, 1861-1862   *DW* 86 and *DW* 95
    Guéraud was a printer and bookseller at Fontenay, and the portrait was
commissioned by Benjamin Fillon, whose portrait Meryon also etched (*DW* 85).
Meryon was supposed to have worked from a photograph for the portrait of
Guéraud, which is etched on a plate, separately from that of the frame. Meryon
etched the portrait on tin, and destroyed it by accident before it could be given to a
printer.[1] The frame is a complicated and not-too-clear allegory of Law, Man,
History, Knowledge and Arcane symbols.[2] The book titles on the frame are of these
topics: Code of Laws, beneath the portrait, Absolute Beauty, Universal Morality,
Perfectibility of Man, Lives of the Saints, Joan of Arc, Table of Logarithms, the
French Victories of Napoleon III, and others. The frame itself exists in numerous
states, with varying changes in the titles of books and papers, to no apparent logic.
Portrait and frame are shown in one of the rare impressions together, from
Toledo (Cat. 106).

106.
Third state with the seventh state of the frame (*DW* 95); very rare, only three other
impressions known
Etching and drypoint: portrait printed in black ink, cleanly wiped; frame printed
in brown ink, full plate tone; both on gray china paper

---

1. Meryon commented on this at the end of *Mes Observations,* adding that "the only impressions existing are those
successive trial proofs, and a very small number of these [two etchings] together, in a rather heavy printing, the
print having already deteriorated. . . ."   2. The portrait was termed "truly hideous" by *Burty and Huish,* 1879,
p. 99; they saw the frame as a representation of the "history and progress of printing," p. 88.

Plate: 165 x 130 mm. (6-5/8 x 5-3/16 in.)
Portrait alone: 54 x 48 mm. (2-3/16 x 1-7/8 in.)

INSCRIPTIONS: Above shoulder: *C.M.*; along bottom: *Meryon. Inv, Sculp. Paris
MDCCCLXII Meryon Imp r Duperé 20*
PROVENANCE: P. Burty (L. 413); J. J. Heywood; B. B. MacGeorge (Wright
inscription)
IMPRESSIONS: Cleveland; New York PL; Paris
Lent by the Toledo Museum of Art (23.3079)

Adresse de Rochoux, 1856   *DW* 87
Address card for Rochoux
   "I have composed, in days gone by, this address card for Monsieur Rochoux,
Printseller. It is etched on two plates, as it must be in order to be printed in red
and black," wrote Meryon in 1863.[1] At the top, (Cat. 107, Wesleyan University)
flanking the gate to the Palais de Justice, are reclining figures representing the Seine
and Marne rivers, from which waters flow down the sides. Below is a row of old
houses, and in the center is the statue of Henri IV on the tip of the Ile de la Cité
atop one span of the Pont Neuf. Below this is a galley and the motto "Fluctuat nec
mergitur." These are subjects from the *Eaux-Fortes sur Paris,* the particular area
on the Ile de la Cité where Rochoux' print shop was located.

107.
Fifth state
Etching: red and black ink on white laid paper
Plate: 91 x 120 mm. (3-5/8 x 4-3/4 in.)

INSCRIPTIONS: Lower left: *C*; lower right: *M.*
PROVENANCE: J. Michelin (L. 1490)
IMPRESSIONS: Boston PL w; Cleveland w; New York 2 w; New York PL w
Lent by the Davision Art Center, Wesleyan University, Middletown, Connecticut

L'Attelage, undated   *DW* 90
The Harness
   An etched poem by Meryon (Cat. 108), from Toledo:

---

1. *Mes Observations,* no. 52.

A horse dragged himself along sadly with lowered head
Because he was old, thin and short-winded.
He was pulling a pitiful and poorly-oiled plough.
It was driven by a pensive man who was spare and bent with age.
I truly pitied this pathetic, rigged harness
And tried to give comfort while passing nearby:
"Weary servants, you will have repose
In the eventide of old age,"
I said to them both.
I had barely finished when they answered in unison:
"No, we look forward to nothing in the mocking future
Either today or tomorrow—ever, for we are simple people.
A poor man and a poor beast.
Enduring our lot, until the end,
We must turn up the soil by the sweat of our brows.
We must enrich our master's patrimony;
We must make the oats grow for others
Rather than eat it ourselves."
Indeed, I said to myself, their fatigue is of no value to them.
Their chores, the sweat of their brows, their time and their woes
Bring them no recompense. Ah! There are in truth some—Too numerous,
Who endure more than they deserve in this life.
What reward is there for their thankless toil?...
Death— this is all one can contemplate.

108.
Only state
Etching: black ink on white paper with plate tone
Plate: 136 x 95 mm. (5-3/8 x 3-3/4 in.)

INSCRIPTIONS:

L'Attelage

Un cheval se trainait triste et tête baissée;
Car il était vieux et maigre et poussif;
Il s'en allait tirant plaintive et mal graissée
Une vieille charrue: un homme tout pensif
La menait; il était maigre et courbé par l'age
Et j'eus pitié vraiment de ce pauvre attelage.—

Et pour les consoler, en passant auprès d'eux
—"Serviteurs fatigués, leur dis-je, tous les deux.
"Vous avez le repos au soir de la vieillesse. . . ."
—Je n'avais pas fini qu'ils répondaient en choeur :
—"Non, nous n'attendons rien, jamais, point de liesse,
"Pour nous, dans l'avenir moqueur,
"Aujourd'hui ni demain ; nous sommes de la plèbe,
"Homme pauvre, pauvre animal.
"Il faut, supportant notre mal,
"Finir en remuant la glèbe
"A la sueur de notre front.
"De notre maitre il faut enfler la patrimoine
"Il faut faire pousser l'avoine :
"D'autre que nous la mangeront."

—Oui, me dis-je, pour eux leurs fatigues sont vaines,
Leurs travaux, leurs sueurs, et leurs temps et leurs peines,
Ne leur rapportent rien.—Ah! c'est qu'en vérité,
Quelques uns, trop nombreux, plus qu'ils n'ont mérité
Souffrent en cette vie, et quelle récompense
De leurs labeurs ingrats ? . . . —La mort, à ce qu'on pense.

PROVENANCE : C. Deering (L. 516)
IMPRESSIONS : Cleveland w ; New York chine ; Wesleyan University w
Lent by the Toledo Museum of Art (31.166)

La Loi Lunaire, 1856   *DW* 91
The Lunar Law

La Loi Solaire, 1855   *DW* 93
The Solar Law

The poems accompanying the *Eaux-Fortes sur Paris* are filled with the imagery of
dark streets, mysterious forces, death and hope. Meryon's constant care for the
inhabitants of the vast metropolis is always touching. After the completion of the
Paris set, he wrote and etched two poems, in which he proposed fanciful laws to aid
the urban dweller, the Solar Law of 1855 (Cat. 111, Toledo), and the Lunar Law
of the following year (Cat. 110, Williamstown). In both, written in quasi-legal
form, Meryon imagines himself to be a great ruler, like Napoleon III, a benevolent
despot eager to improve the lot of his subjects. In the Solar Law, he requires open
space, light and fresh air to counter the bad effects of the old city he depicts in his
prints and drawings : Paris already threatened by Haussmann's renovations. In
the Lunar Law, a strong moralizing tone demands that the populace sleep standing
up in open-faced boxes, conserve fuel and respect the laws of nature by using only
natural light for daily activities.

107

There are two related drawings at the Toledo Museum of Art. Both are studies for the border of the Lunar Law; one for a lion that was never used (Cat. 109), and the other, a study for the top border, includes a portrait medallion at top center. Very few impressions seem to exist of the Lunar Law, which was revised and etched again in another version in 1866 (*DW* 92). The Solar Law is known in only a few more impressions apparently published by Meryon.

Lunar Law

If I were Dictator of some strong Republic (which would not be the case),

First: Since the bedstead of our cities is an article of Idleness and Indulgence; and since the upright position is of all the most noble, recumbency being suitable only for the Sick and Dead; I would forbid the usage of the aforesaid couch throughout my nation, obliging ladies and gentlemen to sleep upright and out-of-doors in niches driven vertically into the earth, bearing down upon those closed up within them, holding them in rigid restraint with only the open side turned toward the Eastern Light so that morning's dawn might touch them with its rays.

Second: Since Night wishes for Rest and Silence, and the Moon is its natural torch and since all nocturnal work is, moreover, injurious to the well-being of soul and body; I would forbid every artificial means of prolonging the day, tolerating only sufficient light as would be necessary for everyday activities, to economize on useful substances consumed in burning as well as for conservation of the organs of Breath and Life.

This Law, powerful source of Force and Purity, would be called
The Lunar Law

Solar Law

If I were
Emperor or King
of some powerful state
(which I neither would nor could be);—
Seeing that the Great Cities are born only
For Sloth, Greed, Fear
Luxury and other evil passions;
I would establish a law determining, as precisely
as possible, a portion of land, cultivated or not
to surround, of necessity, every dwelling place

108

of desired size required for a given number of
human beings; in such a way that the Air and the Sun,
these two essential life principles, be always
there to be generously portioned out.

This law, source of all well-being, both material
and consequently moral, would be called
The Solar Law

109.
Study for an unrealized figure of a lion in the etching *La Loi Lunaire*
Pencil on japan paper, laid down
82 x 117 mm. (3-1/4 x 4-5/8 in.)

INSCRIPTIONS: *Loi Lunaire*
PROVENANCE: F. Seymour Haden (initials); F. Carrington, N. Y. 1923
BIBLIOGRAPHY: *Grigaut*, 1950, p. 234, no. 21 (repr.); *Rogers TMN*, 1963, p. 29
(repr.); *Rogers*, 1963, p. 3 (repr.)
Lent by the Toledo Museum of Art (23.3118)

110.
Undescribed third state (identical with Delteil's second state)
Etching: black ink on white paper, touched by the artist with watercolor (only such
proof known)
Plate: 159 x 240 mm. (6-1/4 x 9-7/16 in.)

INSCRIPTIONS:

La Loi Lunaire

Si j'étais
Dictateur
de
Quelque forte République
(Ce qui ne saurait être)
Vu 1°: que le lit de nos Cités est meuble de Paresse et de Luxure;
. . . que la position droite est de toutes la plus noble,
que celle couchée ne convient qu'aux Infirmes et aux Morts;
. . . Interdirais: l'usage du dit meuble dans toute l'étendue de mes Etats
. . . forçant Hommes et Femmes à dormir . . . Debout et Dehors . . .
dans des niches verticales, fichées en terre, tangentes
à ceux y renfermés, les tenant en strict respect, la seule face
libre, tournée vers le Levant, pour que l'aube matinale

les frappât de sa lumière.

Vu 2° : que la Nuit veut Repos et Silence ; . . . que la Lune en est le
flambeau naturel . . . que toute oeuvre
nocturne est à la fois préjudiciable au parfait état de l'âme et
du corps : . . . Interdirais : tout moyen factice de
prolonger le jour, . . . ne tolérant que les feux strictement nécessaires
aux us de la vie, tant pour économie de substances
utiles, qui se consomment vainement en fumée, que dans un but
conservateur des organes du Souffle et de la Vue
Cette loi, cause puissante de Force et de Pureté, s' appellerait,

Loi Lunaire

C. Meryon fit.   Paris MDCCLVI   Imp. R.F. St Jacques No. 81

111.
Only state
Etching and drypoint : red and black ink on ivory wove paper
Plate : 121 x 83 mm. (4-5/8 x 3-3/16 in.)

INSCRIPTIONS :

La Loi Solaire

Si j'étais
Empereur ou Roi
de quelque puissant état
(ce que je ne voudrais ni ne pourrais être) ;—
Vu que les Grandes Cités ne sont enfantées
que pour la Paresse, l'Avarice, la Crainte,
La Luxure et autres mauvaises passions ; je fe-
rais élaborer une loi délorminant [sic], d'une manière aussi précise que possible, l'èspace de terrain, avec ou
sans culture, forcément adjoint à toute habitation
de capacité voulue, pour un nombre donné de créatures
humaines ; de telle sorte que l'Air et le Soleil
ces deux principes essentiels de la Vie, pus-

> sent toujours y être largement repartis.
> Cette loi, source de tout bien-être maté-
> riel et conséquemment moral, s'appellerait
> Loi Solaire

C. Meryon fit   Paris MDCCCIV
                    Imp. R. F. S. Jacques 31.

IMPRESSIONS: Boston; Cleveland; Cambridge (Fitzwilliam); London 2; New York 3; New York PL; Paris
Lent by the Toledo Museum of Art (24.25)

112.
Anonymous, German, ca. 1840
La Morgue in Paris, after C. Reiss
Etching and engraving
Image: 94 x 147 mm. (3-11/16 x 5-13/16 in.)
Lent by the Yale University Art Gallery (1973.9.56)

113.
Auguste-Henry Berthoud (1829-1887), after Jacques Testard (1810-after 1870)
La Morgue
Etching and aquatint
Image: 105 x 168 mm. (4-1/8 x 6-5/8 in.)
Lent by the Fry Print Collection, Yale University Medical Library

Meryon Collectors

Philippe Burty (1830-1890) Paris, author and art critic

   An amateur artist at the outset of his career, Burty wrote extensively and persuasively on contemporary etching, which he assiduously collected. He published catalogues on the work of Millet (1861), Meissonier (1862), Meryon (1863), Seymour Haden (1866), Rousseau (1867), and Célestin Nanteuil (1877) along with numerous articles and books. Burty was an early and enthusiastic collector of Japanese art along with Jules and Edmund Goncourt. He met and befriended Meryon about 1856 and based his articles on a knowledge of the artist as his friend. Along with Jules Niel, he was probably the most discerning of Meryon's early collectors. In 1876, the bulk of his Meryon collection was sold at auction by Sotheby and Co., London. He was appointed Inspector of Fine Arts in 1881.

Hippolyte-Alexandre Destailleur (1822-1893) Paris, architect

A noted architect of the period and architect for the Ministry of Justice in 1853.
As a collector, Destailleur was particularly interested in works of art concerning
Paris from the 18th century to his own time.

Sir Francis Seymour Haden (1818-1910) London, physician and printmaker

In 1847, Seymour Haden began to etch and became Whistler's brother-in-law.
He was a close friend of Whistler and founded the Society of Painter-Etchers
in 1880. He probably met Meryon in Paris in the late 1850s, and purchased prints
from him for the Victoria and Albert Museum. A fine draughtsman/etcher in his
own right, he is considered one of the best judges of the quality of an impression.

J. J. Heywood (?-1887) London, Protestant minister

He owned a fine, but not large, collection of Meryon prints and drawings made
by careful purchases at the Niel and Burty sales in London (1873-1879).
Heywood's collection was sold to Ellis and White, London, in 1879, then to
Thibaudeau, and thence to MacGeorge.

Bernard Buchanan MacGeorge (?-1924) Glasgow, stockbroker

Probably the largest private collection of Meryon's work ever assembled
belonged to B. B. MacGeorge, comprising the rarest proofs and numerous drawings.
Most items were from the collection of Reverend J. J. Heywood, purchased with
the aid of A. W. Thibaudeau around 1880. The entire MacGeorge Collection was
purchased in 1916 by P. & D. Colnaghi and Obach of London, who offered the
Meryons en bloc to the British Museum. The museum was unable to purchase the
collection, and it passed to M. Knoedler & Co. in New York.

Howard Mansfield (1849-?) New York, attorney

He was best known for his great and complete collection of Whistler prints.
In 1877, he began collecting Meryon prints which he sold to the Art Institute
of Chicago in 1909. With MacGeorge, Mansfield's was one of the most complete
collections of Meryon's work.

Jules Niel (?-1873) Paris, professional civil servant, Ministry of the Interior

One of the posts Niel held was that of head of the department of urban roads;
he was also in charge of many urban monuments from 1839 until 1848, when
he became librarian of the Ministry. He collected prints and drawings of all periods,
including contemporary, and was one of the first to buy and appreciate Meryon's

work. He arranged for the Ministry to buy sets of the *Eaux-Fortes sur Paris*. He became a close friend of the artist and arranged for him to meet the Duc d'Arenberg. The Goncourt brothers expressed their admiration for his extensive collection in 1856. Niel's daughter, Gabrielle, studied etching with Meryon and formed a large collection of the artist's work as well.

Gustave Adolphe Salicis (?-1889) naval officer

Like Meryon, Salicis' education prepared him for a career in the Navy. After attending the Ecole Polytechnique (see Cats. 76-79), he became a seaman first class; in 1842, he and Meryon met on the *Rhin* voyage to New Zealand and became close and sympathetic companions, sharing duties and interests such as astronomy, meteorology and cartography. Salicis transferred from the *Rhin* in Tahiti; their careers diverged from there although they remained fast friends. Salicis attained the rank of Captain and remained in the Navy until 1857, when he left the sea to become a teacher at L'Ecole Polytechnique. Through his association with L'Ecole des Beaux-Arts, he remained in touch with Meryon's career, commissioned and purchased his work, and eulogized Meryon at the artist's gravesite at Charenton in 1868.

A. W. Thibaudeau (ca. 1840-1892) Paris and London, print dealer and author

In collaboration with Poulet-Malassis (Baudelaire's publisher), he wrote a monograph on Alphonse Legros (1877), whose work he sold in London along with that of Meryon, Bracquemond and others. After gambling losses and some concurrent financial troubles, he left for the United States in 1889 where he died soon thereafter, an employee of a railroad.

Fig. 1. Leopold Flameng: *Charles Meryon Sitting in Bed*. Heliogravure after a drawing

Fig. 2. Charles Negre: *Henri Le Secq at Notre-Dame*. Photograph, ca. 1851.
    Courtesy of Metropolitan Museum of Art

Fig. 3. Anonymous French photographer: *Pont et Pompe Notre-Dame.*
Daguerreotype, ca. 1855. Courtesy of Metropolitan Museum of Art

Fig. 4. Charles Meryon: *Preparatory Study for L'Abside de Notre-Dame*.
Private Collection, New York

PLATES

Cat. 1

F. Bracquemond: *Portrait of Charles Meryon*
Beraldi 77
Toledo Museum of Art

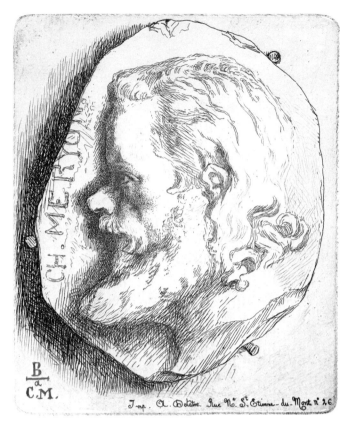

Cat. 3

Portrait of Charles Meryon
DW 17A, third state
Toledo Museum of Art

Cat. 2

Title : *Eaux-Fortes sur Paris*
DW 17, only state
Toledo Museum of Art

Cat. 4

Dédicace à Reinier Nooms, Dit Zéeman
DW 18, only state
Toledo Museum of Art

Cat. 6

Armes Symboliques de la Ville de Paris
DW 21, third state
Davison Art Center, Wesleyan University

Cat. 5

Ancienne Porte du Palais de Justice
DW 19, third state
Toledo Museum of Art

Cat. 7

Fluctuat nec mergitur
DW 22, only state
Toledo Museum of Art

Cat. 8

Le Stryge: Study of the Chimera and the Tower of St. Jacques, pencil drawing
Sterling and Francine Clark Art Institute, Williamstown

Cat. 9

Le Stryge: Study of the City and the Birds, pencil drawing
Sterling and Francine Clark Art Institute, Williamstown

Cat. 10

Le Stryge
DW 23, first state
Fogg Art Museum, Harvard University

Cat. 12

Le Stryge
DW 23, fourth state
Yale University Art Gallery

LE STRYGE

Cat. 13

Le Stryge
DW 23, eighth state
Museum of Art, Carnegie Institute, Pittsburgh

Cat. 14

Le Petit Pont: First study, made with a 'camera lucida'
Pencil drawing
Toledo Museum of Art

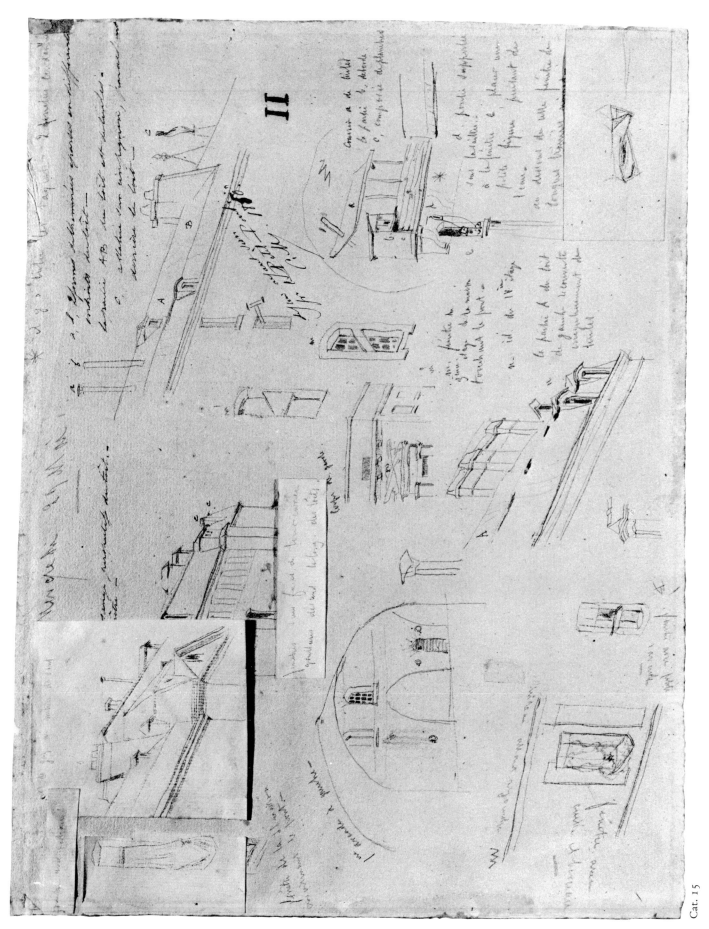

Cat. 15

Le Petit Pont: Study for details of bridge and houses, pencil drawing   Toledo Museum of Art

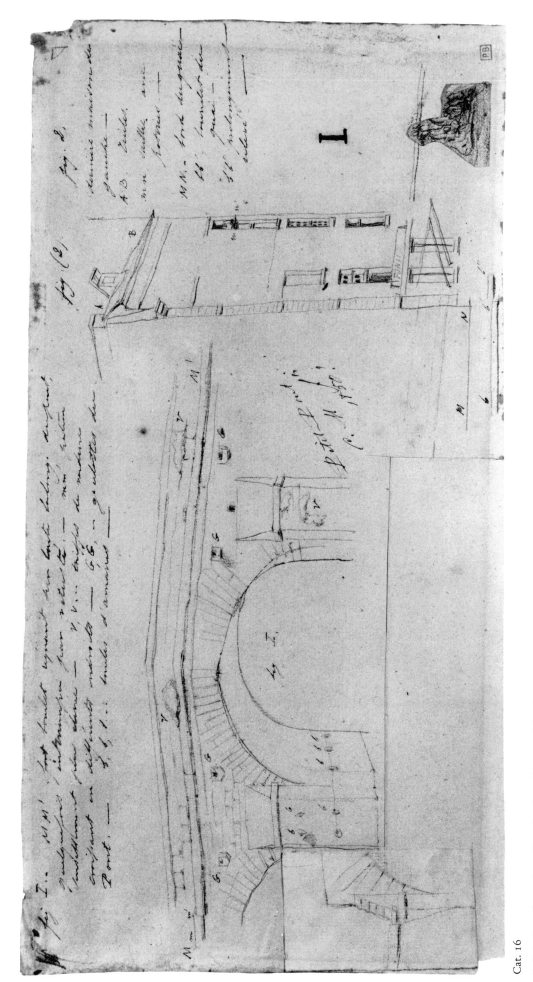

Cat. 16

Le Petit Pont: Sheet of pencil studies for architectural details
Toledo Museum of Art

Cat. 17

Le Petit Pont   DW 24, first state   Lent Anonymously

Le Petit Pont

Cat. 19

Le Petit Pont   DW 24, fifth state   Philadelphia Museum of Art

Cat. 20

L' Arche du Pont Notre-Dame: First study, made with a 'camera lucida'
Pencil, pen and ink on tracing paper
Art Institute of Chicago

Cat. 21

L' Arche du Pont Notre-Dame: Preparatory pencil study
Museum of Art, Carnegie Institute, Pittsburgh

L'Arche du Pont Notre-Dame: Pencil study for background   Toledo Museum of Art

Cat. 23

L' Arche du Pont Notre-Dame: Final pencil drawing
Sterling and Francine Clark Art Institute, Williamstown

Cat. 24

L'Arche du Pont Notre-Dame
DW 25, first state
Fogg Art Museum, Harvard University

C. Meryon Del. sculp. imp. Rue N.º S.ᵗ Etienne du Mont 26.   Paris 1853

Cat. 25

L'Arche du Pont Notre-Dame
DW 25, fourth state
Yale University Art Gallery

Cat. 26

La Galerie Notre-Dame: Preparatory pencil drawing
Art Institute of Chicago

LA GALERIE N·D·

Cat. 28

La Galerie Notre-Dame   DW 26, fifth state   Yale University Art Gallery

Cat. 29

La Rue des Mauvais Garçons
DW 27, third state
Boston Public Library

Cat. 30

La Tour de l'Horloge: Preliminary pencil drawing
Metropolitan Museum of Art

Cat. 31

La Tour de l'Horloge: Pencil study for a Seine barge
Toledo Museum of Art

Cat. 32

La Tour de l'Horloge: Preliminary pencil and red chalk drawing
Toledo Museum of Art

Cat. 33

La Tour de l'Horloge   DW 28, third state   Yale University Art Gallery

Cat. 34

La Tour de l'Horloge
DW 28, eighth state
Worcester Art Museum

Cat. 35

Tourelle de la Rue de la Tixéranderie: Preliminary pencil drawing
Museum of Art, Carnegie Institute, Pittsburgh

Cat. 36

Tourelle de la Rue de la Tixéranderie: Final pencil drawing
Art Institute of Chicago

Cat. 38

Tourelle de la Rue de la Tixéranderie   DW 29, second state   Museum of Art, Carnegie Institute, Pittsburgh

Cat. 39

Saint-Etienne-du-Mont: Pencil study for side of Collège de Montaigu
Toledo Museum of Art

Cat. 40

Saint-Etienne-du-Mont: Pencil study for Collège de Montaigu
Toledo Museum of Art

Cat. 41

Saint-Etienne-du-Mont: Final preparatory drawing
Toledo Museum of Art

Cat. 43

Saint-Etienne-du-Mont DW 30, fourth state St. Louis Art Museum

Cat. 47

La Petite Pompe
DW 32, second state
Museum of Art, Carnegie Institute, Pittsburgh

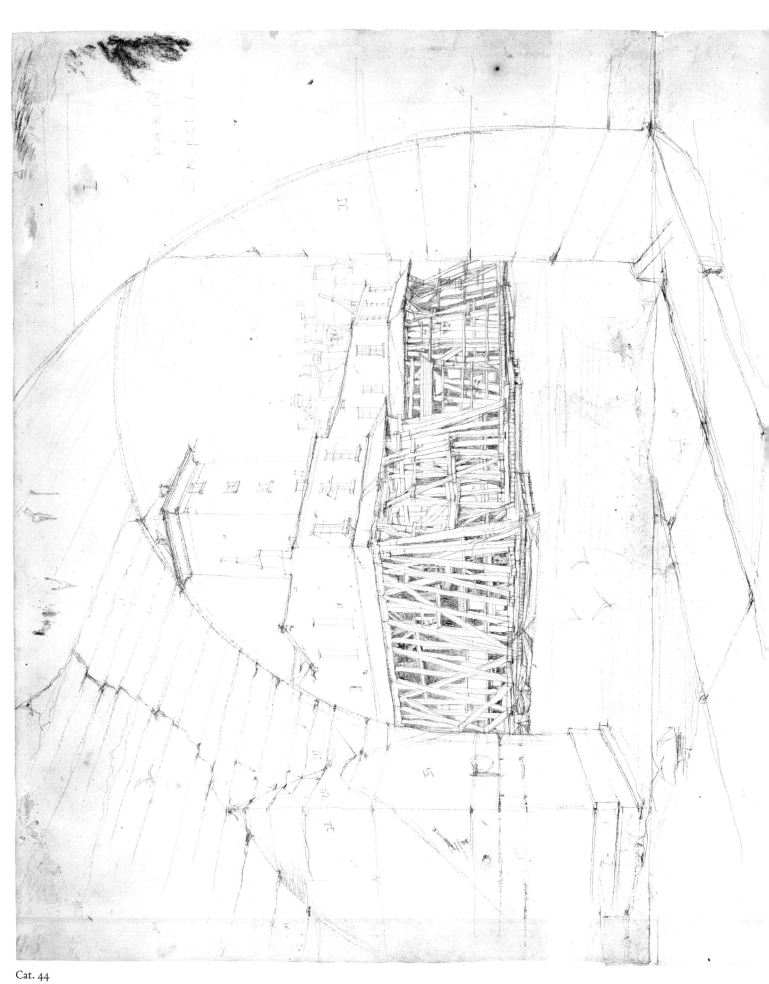

Cat. 44

La Pompe Notre-Dame: Preliminary pencil study
Museum of Fine Arts, Boston

Cat. 46

La Pompe Notre-Dame
DW 31, sixth state
Detroit Institute of Arts

Cat. 48

Le Pont-Neuf: Preliminary pencil drawing
Toledo Museum of Art

Cat. 49

Le Pont-Neuf
DW 33, second state
Art Institute of Chicago

Cat. 50

Le Pont-Neuf
DW 33, sixth state
Toledo Museum of Art

LE PONT-NEUF.

Cat. 51

Le Pont-Neuf
DW 33, ninth state
Yale University Art Gallery

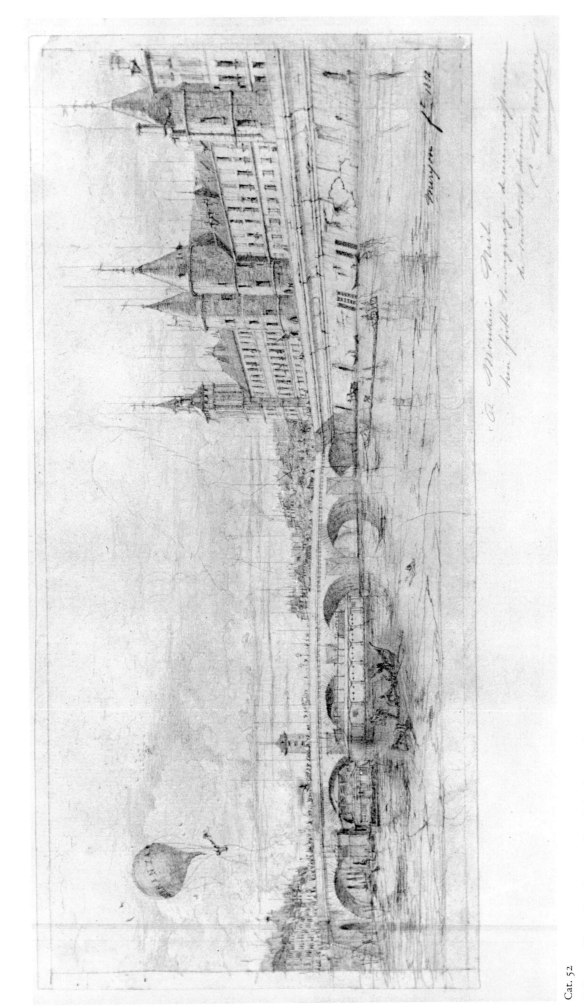

Cat. 52

Le Pont-au-Change: Complete pencil study for the second state
Sterling and Francine Clark Art Institute, Williamstown

Cat. 53

Le Pont-au-Change: Anthropomorphic cloud studies (second version), pencil
Sterling and Francine Clark Art Institute, Williamstown

Cat. 54

Le Pont-au-Change
DW 34, first state
National Gallery of Art, Rosenwald Collection

Cat. 55

Le Pont-au-Change
DW 34, second state
Fogg Art Museum, Harvard University

Cat. 56

Le Pont-au-Change
DW 34, fifth state
St. Louis Art Museum

Cat. 57

Le Pont-au-Change
DW 34, seventh state
Metropolitan Museum of Art

Cat. 58

Le Pont-au-Change
DW 34, tenth state
Minneapolis Institute of Arts

LE PONT-AU-CHANGE.

Cat. 59

Le Pont-au-Change
DW 34, eleventh state
Philadelphia Museum of Art

Cat. 71

Le Tombeau de Molière
DW 40, second state
Toledo Museum of Art

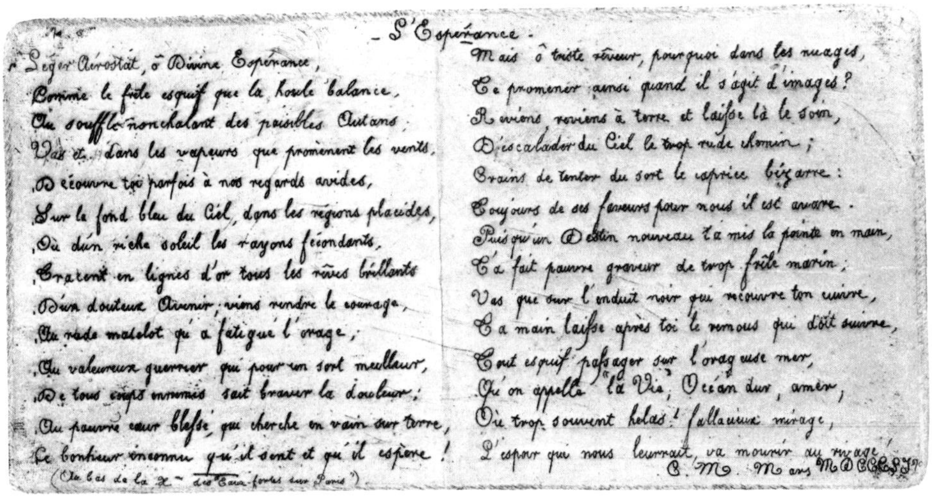

— L'Espérance —

Léger Aérostat, ô Divine Espérance,
Comme le frêle esquif que la houle balance,
Au souffle nonchalant des paisibles Autans,
Vas et dans les vapeurs que promènent les vents,
Découvre toi parfois à nos regards avides,
Sur le fond bleu du Ciel, dans les régions placides,
Où d'un riche soleil les rayons fécondants,
Tracent en lignes d'or tous les rêves brillants
D'un douteux Avenir; viens rendre le courage,
Au rude matelot qu'a fatigué l'orage,
Au valeureux guerrier qui pour un sort meilleur,
De tous coups ennemis sait braver la douleur;
Au pauvre cœur blessé qui cherche en vain sur terre,
Le bonheur inconnu qu'il sent et qu'il espère!
(Au bas de la Xme des "Eaux-fortes sur Paris")

Mais ô triste rêveur, pourquoi dans les nuages,
Te promener ainsi quand il s'agit d'images?
Reviens reviens à terre et laisse là le soin,
D'escalader du Ciel le trop rude chemin;
Crains de tenter du sort le caprice bizarre:
Toujours de ses faveurs pour nous il est avare.
Puisqu'un Destin nouveau t'a mis la pointe en main,
T'a fait pauvre graveur de trop frêle marin;
Vas que sur l'enduit noir qui recouvre ton cuivre,
Ta main laisse après toi le remous qui doit suivre,
Tout esquif passager sur l'orageuse mer,
Qu'on appelle "la Vie", Océan dur, amer,
Où trop souvent hélas! fallacieux mirage,
L'espoir qui nous leurrait, va mourir au rivage!
C. M. Mars MDCCCLIV

Cat. 61

L'Espérance
DW 35, second state
Toledo Museum of Art

Cat. 62

La Morgue
DW 36, first state
National Gallery of Art, Rosenwald Collection

C. Meryon del. sculp. mdccliv.

Imp. Rue neuve St. Etienne du Mont. n° 26.

Cat. 63

La Morgue
DW 36, fourth state (with DW 37)
Museum of Art, Carnegie Institute, Pittsburgh

Cat. 64

La Morgue
DW 36, fourth state
Cleveland Museum of Art

Cat. 66

Edmond Gosselin: *La Morgue*
Davison Art Center, Wesleyan University

Cat. 67

L'Abside de Notre Dame: Drawing of Notre-Dame with the north side of the Ile de la Cité
Yale University Art Gallery

Cat. 68

L'Abside de Notre-Dame
DW 38, first state
National Gallery of Art, Rosenwald Collection

Cat. 69

L'Abside de Notre-Dame
DW 38, fourth state
Cleveland Museum of Art

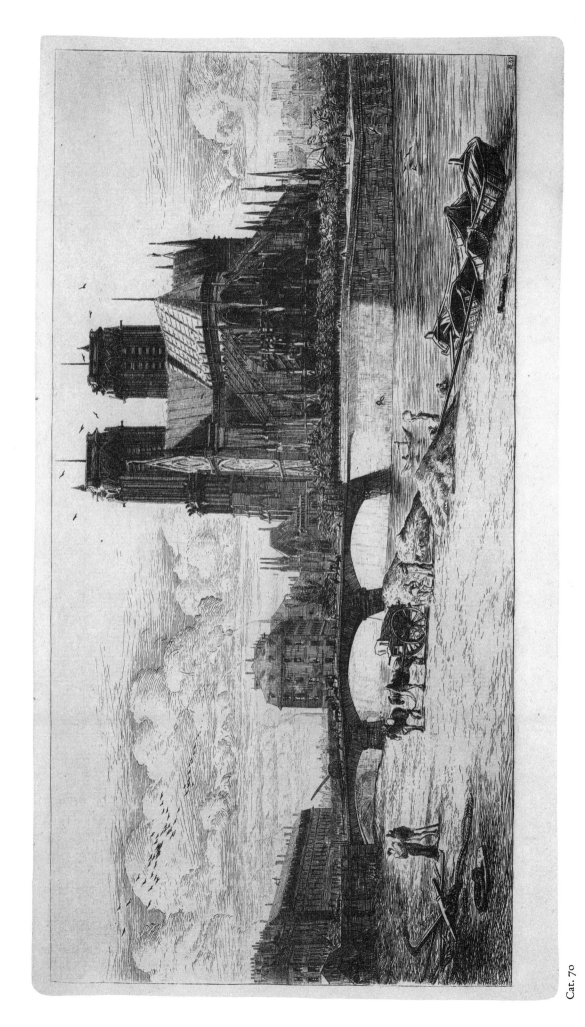

Cat. 70

Edmond Gosselin: *L'Abside de Notre-Dame*
Davison Art Center, Wesleyan University

Cat. 73

La Rue des Chantres: Study for the spire, pencil
Toledo Museum of Art

Cat. 72

Tourelle, Rue de l'École-de-Médecine
DW 41, between ninth and tenth states
Cleveland Museum of Art

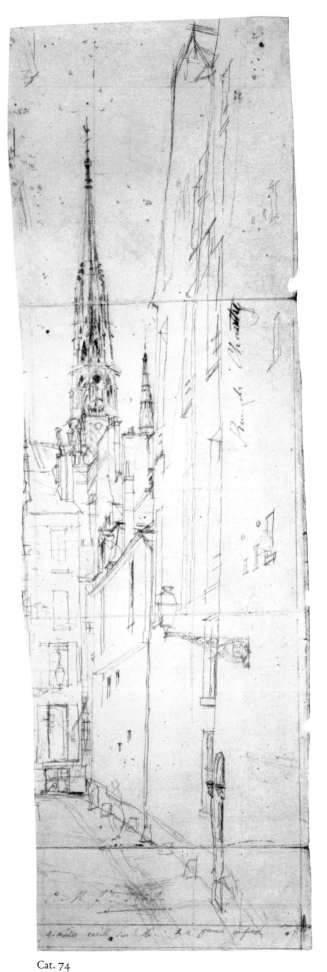

Cat. 74

La Rue des Chantres: Pencil study for the print
Toledo Museum of Art

Cat. 75

La Rue des Chantres   DW 42, fifth state   Yale University Art Gallery

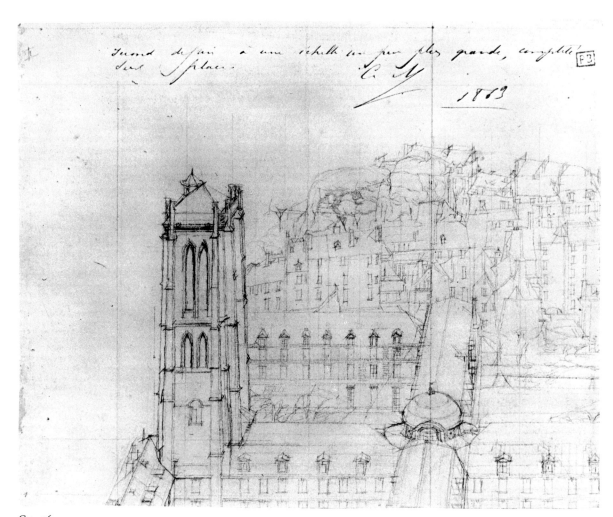

Cat. 76

Collège Henri IV: Study for upper left section
National Gallery of Art, Rosenwald Collection

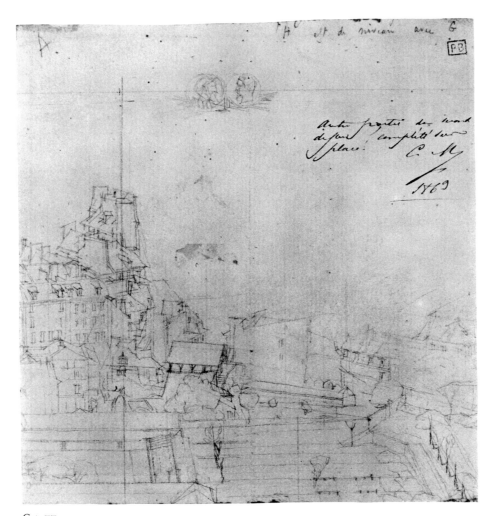

Cat. 77

Collège Henri IV: Study for upper center section
National Gallery of Art, Rosenwald Collection

COLLÈGE HENRI IV OU LYCÉE NAPOLÉON, AVEC SES DÉPENDANCES ET CONSTRUCTIONS VOISINES.

Cette pièce qui, à notre sens, a un côté très sérieux indépendamment de quelques particularités ayant trait à son exécution, que nous passerons ici sous silence, les quelles peuvent lui prêter de l'intérêt, n'est pas rester terminée comme il est facile de le voir malgré corrections devant y être faites mais nous estimons même quelle ce nombre dépreuves [...] de cet état spécial que nous avons désiré dans cette pensée à ces adeptes entièrement dévouées à la cause une et absolue du VRAI et du BIEN ayant pour nous quelque amplitude [...] avec nos maladresses bien apparentes ici, nous aussi intérêt, encore pour la rustique [...] espérant que ce présent mode d'expression de notre manière de voir, luxure et fort risque mais le sentons mais sincère [...] trouvera accès auprès d'eux à ile veulent bien prendre la peine d'interpréter les choses que nous voudu figurées et au dessus de la représentation positive mais en reposant pour les meilleures conclusions de part pris auprès quasi, surtout plus grande pénétration amener volonté et force, et est tout enfin sur leur plus parfait état de grâce auprès du Bien Maître qui nous guide dans les approchons de notre esprit, dans nos déterminations en avec ici ba nos vœux, et nous donne assistance pour la réalisation de nos entreprises.

Paris, ce 15 Janvier 1864

Imp. Lemercier, r. de Seine 57.   Paris, 1864, DIDIOT, Quai de l'Horloge 19

Cat. 78

Collège Henri IV
DW 43, fourth state
Bowdoin College Museum of Art

Cat. 79

Collège Henri IV
DW 43, tenth state
Davison Art Center, Wesleyan University

Cat. 80

Le Ministère de la Marine: Two pencil studies for the print
Fogg Art Museum, Harvard University

Cat. 81

Le Ministère de la Marine
DW 45, fifth state
Philadelphia Museum of Art

Cat. 82

Rue Pirouette aux Halles: Preparatory pencil drawing
Museum of Art, Carnegie Institute, Pittsburgh

Cat. 83

Rue Pirouette aux Halles
DW 49, third state
National Gallery of Art, Rosenwald Collection

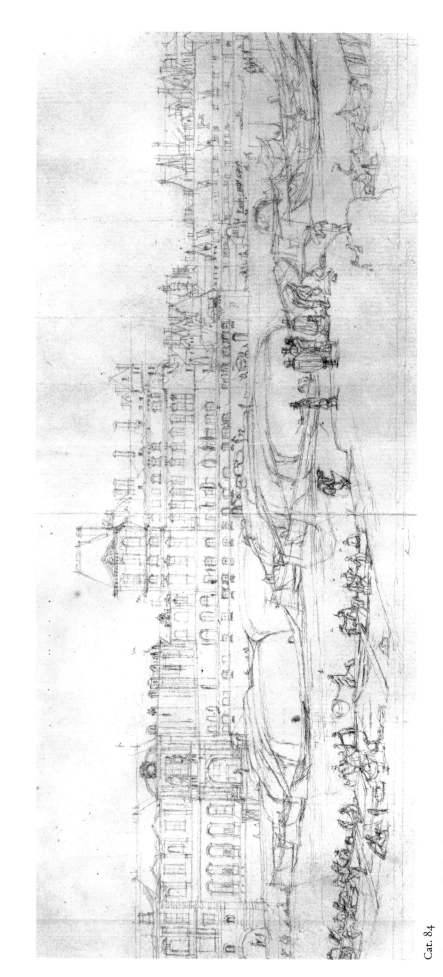

Cat. 84

L'Ancin Louvre, d'après Zéeman: Preparatory pencil drawing
Bowdoin College Museum of Art

Cat. 85

L'Ancien Louvre, d'après Zéeman
DW 53, fifth state
Museum of Art, Carnegie Institute, Pittsburgh

Cat. 86

Porte d'un Ancien Couvent à Bourges
DW 54, second state
Toledo Museum of Art

Cat. 87

La Rue des Toiles à Bourges: Preliminary pencil study
Art Institute of Chicago

Cat. 88

La Rue des Toiles à Bourges
DW 55, sixth state
Museum of Art, Carnegie Institute, Pittsburgh

Cat. 89

Ancienne Habitation à Bourges: Preparatory pencil drawing
Sterling and Francine Clark Art Institute, Williamstown

Cat. 90

Ancienne Habitation à Bourges
DW 56, third state
Boston Public Library

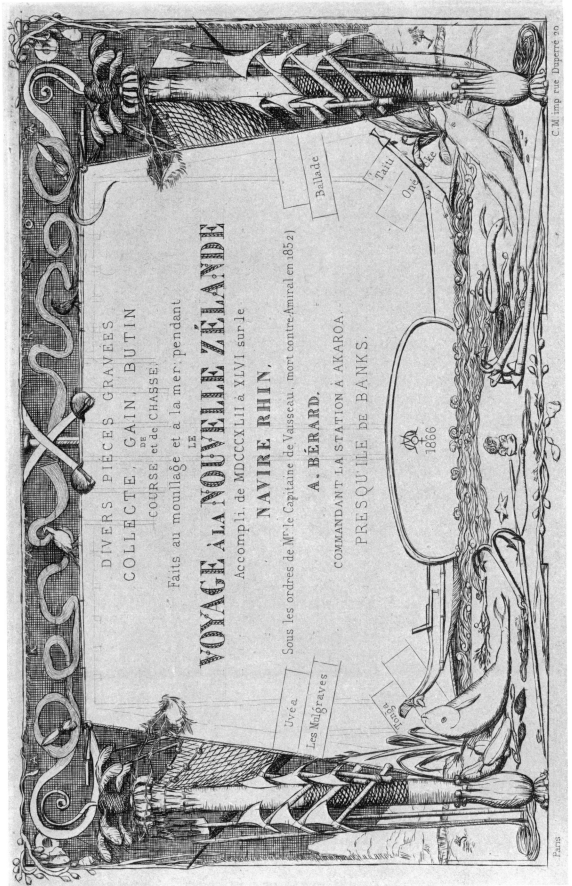

DIVERS PIÈCES GRAVÉES
COLLECTE, GAIN, BUTIN
DE
COURSE et de CHASSE,
Faits au mouillage et à la mer; pendant
LE
VOYAGE À LA NOUVELLE ZÉLANDE
Accompli, de MDCCCXLII à XLVI sur le
NAVIRE RHIN,
Sous les ordres de Mr. le Capitaine de Vaisseau, mort contre-Amiral en 1852
A. BÉRARD.
COMMANDANT LA STATION À AKAROA.
PRESQU'ILE DE BANKS.

Ballade

Taïti

Oné...cke

Jvéa

Les Mulgraves

Tonga

1866

Paris

C.M. imp rue Duperré 20

Cat. 91

Couverture du Voyage à la Nouvelle Zélande
DW 63, eighth state
Toledo Museum of Art

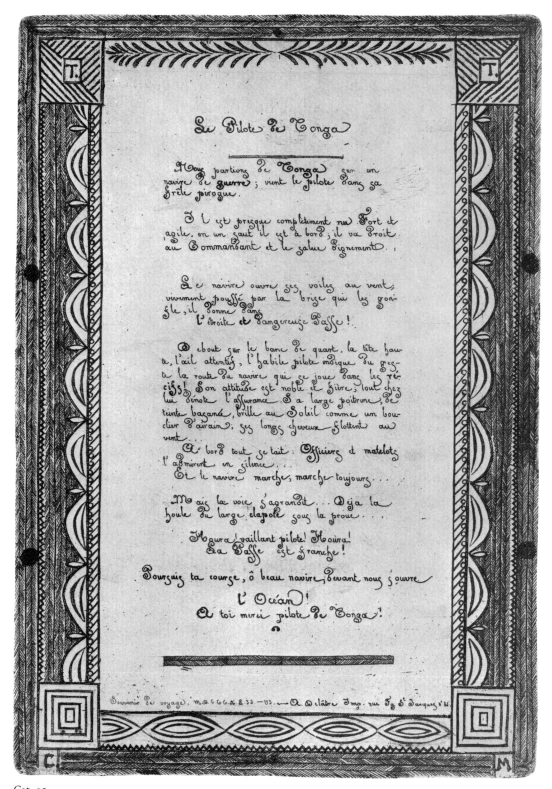

Cat. 92

Le Pilote de Tonga
DW 64, second state
Toledo Museum of Art

Cat. 93

Océanie, Pêche aux Palmes
DW 68, fourth state
Museum of Art, Carnegie Institute, Pittsburgh

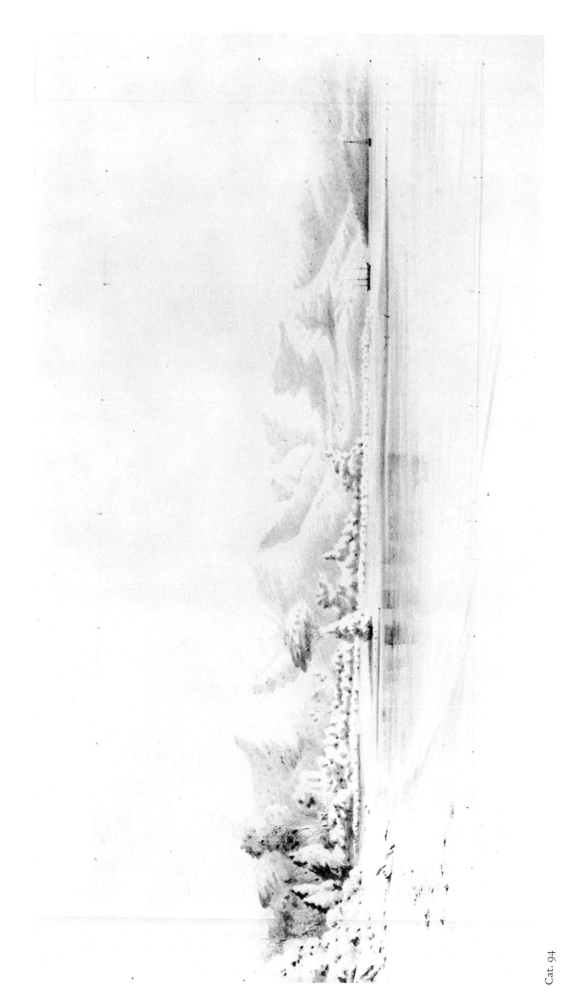

Cat. 94

Presqu'île de Banks, Pointe des Charbonniers, Akaroa: Original study made on the site
Minneapolis Institute of Arts

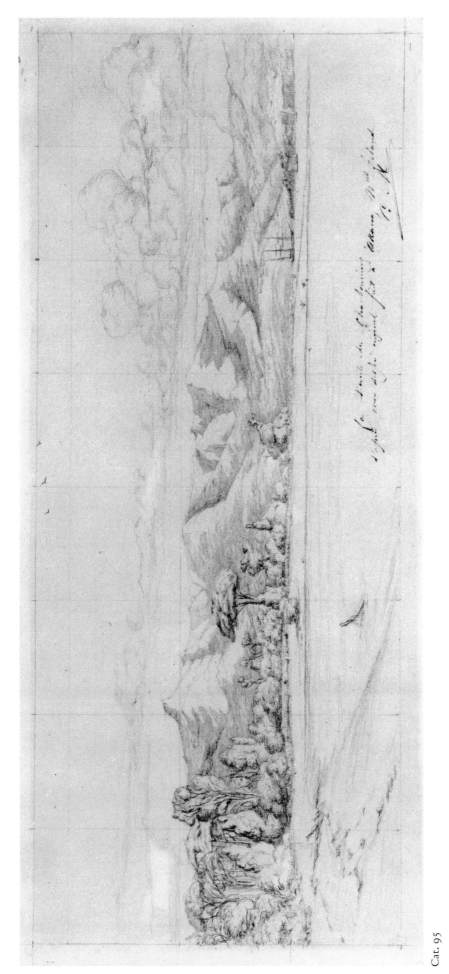

Cat. 95

Presqu'île de Banks, Pointe des Charbonniers, Akaroa: Final pencil study
Toledo Museum of Art

Voyage du Rhin.

NOUVELLE ZÉLANDE. Presqu'il de BANKS . 1845.

Pointe dite des Charbonniers, à AKAROA. Pêche à la Seine.

Cat. 96

Presqu'île de Banks, Pointe des Charbonniers, Akaroa
DW 69, fourth state
Davison Art Center, Wesleyan University

Cat. 97

Case Abandonné: Pencil study of an Abandoned Hut, Akaroa
Toledo Museum of Art

LA CHAUMIÈRE DU COLON VIEUX-SOLDAT
A AKAROA (N^elle ZÉLANDE)
1845

Cat. 99

La Chaumière du Colon
DW 72, third state
Toledo Museum of Art

Cat. 100

"*Daguerreotypes*" *of San Francisco* (1)   The Art Institute of Chicago

Cat. 100

"Daguerreotypes" of San Francisco (2)   The Art Institute of Chicago

Cat 100

"Daguerreotypes" of San Francisco (3)   The Art Institute of Chicago

Cat. 100

"Daguerreotypes" of San Francisco (4)   The Art Institute of Chicago

Cat. 100

"Daguerreotypes" of San Francisco (5)   The Art Institute of Chicago

San Francisco: Pencil study for pastures   Art Institute of Chicago

Cat. 102

San Francisco: Pencil study of horses and riders
Sterling and Francine Clark Art Institute, Williamstown

Cat. 103

San Francisco
DW 73, third state
Yale University Art Gallery

Cat. 105

Casimir le Conte   DW 77, second state   Museum of Art, Carnegie Institute, Pittsburgh

Cat. 106

Armand Guéraud
DW 86, third state and DW 95, seventh state
Toledo Museum of Art

Cat. 107

Adresse de Rochoux
DW 87, fifth state
Davison Art Center, Wesleyan University

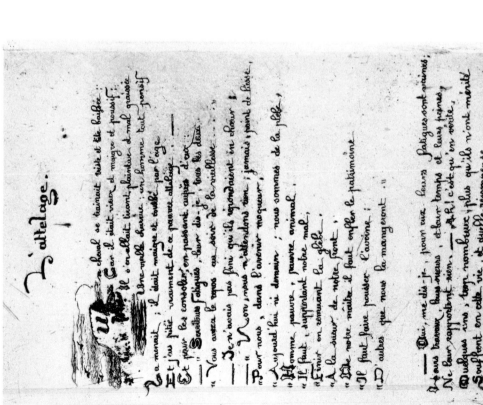

Cat. 108

L'Attelage
DW 90, only state
Toledo Museum of Art

Cat. 109

La Loi Lunaire: Study for an unrealized figure of a lion
Toledo Museum of Art

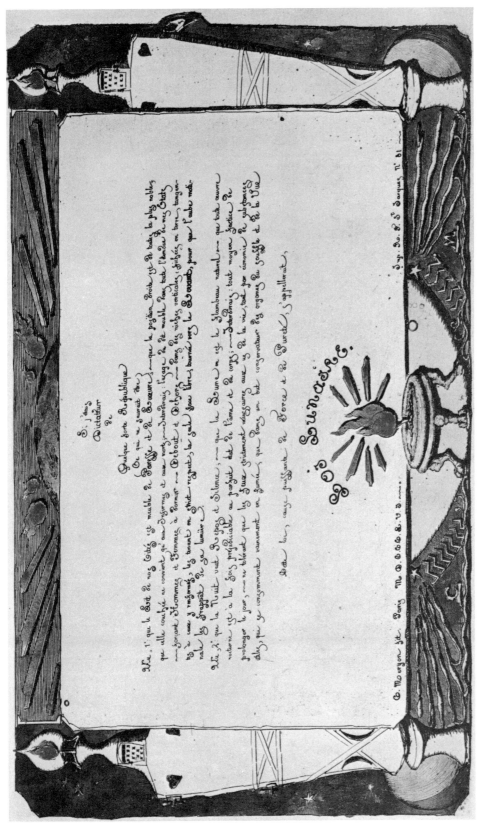

Cat. 110

La Loi Lunaire
DW 91, undescribed third state
Sterling and Francine Clark Art Institute, Williamstown

Cat. 111

La Loi Solaire
DW 93, only state
Toledo Museum of Art